THIS ISLAND'S MINE

A fisherman mending his net

THIS ISLAND'S MINE

by

WILFRED FOWLER

THE ADVENTURERS CLUB

LONDON

THE ADVENTURERS CLUB
178-202 Great Portland Street, London, W.1

Printed in Great Britain
by T. and A. Constable Ltd., Hopetoun Street,
Printers to the University of Edinburgh

Contents

Contents

List of Illustrations

"The Solomon Islands, lying between the parallels of 5 and 12 South and the meridians of about 154½ and 162½ East, consist of a double row of mountainous islands. . . .

"In appearance the islands present many similar characteristics; the lofty mountains are for the most part clothed with dense forests and rank undergrowth, which here and there give place to long grass and ferns. The larger islands are well watered by numerous rivulets, at the mouths of which, as well as on the swamps and sandy shores of uninhabited coral islets, crocodiles abound.

"Some of these islands are entirely of volcanic formation, while others are calcareous, but there are also many cases in which both these formations are combined."

Pacific Islands—Sailing Directions.

CHAPTER ONE

Ysabel

THE friendly man who talked to me on a wet December day in London told me that appointments for West Africa were made in August, then he added, "Would you like to go to the Solomon Islands?"

"I don't know," I said, surprised by his question. "I don't know where they are or anything about them."

He took a pointer and turned to a wall map, touching a few dots off the end of New Guinea.

"There they are," he said.

He laid the pointer on the table and faced me again. I searched my memory for something to say. "Weren't they in the news a short time ago?" I asked.

"Yes, two administrative officers and some native police were murdered on the island of Malaita last year. The murderers were rounded up by a local volunteer force. There was a trial; some survivors gave evidence and six natives were condemned and executed and some others were sent to prison." He glanced at his watch. "Would you like some tea?" he suggested.

We drank tea and ate buns and he asked me about myself. He said nothing more about the Solomon Islands until I got up to go.

"Would you accept an appointment in the Solomons if it were offered you?" he asked.

August was a long way off. I felt a bond of sympathy with this agreeable man.

"Yes, I think I would," I replied.

This Island's Mine

I sailed from Tilbury in the Orient steamer *Orford*, through the Mediterranean, down the Red Sea and across the Indian Ocean. At Sydney I parted from a dozen jolly people, sure that we were friends for life. Nine days later I went down to Wooloomooloo to embark in the *Mataram*. There were thirty passengers—missionaries, planters, traders and a few officials going back to work. I shared a cabin with another cadet, a tall good-looking man named Anderson.

On the seventh day out of Sydney, when sea birds appeared high in the sky, I saw a coconut bobbing about in the froth of the bow wave. It was a dull day and the sky was only a shade lighter grey than the sea. On the horizon an amorphous low-lying mass might have been a cloud, but the outline became more irregular the nearer we steamed and a silhouette of trees appeared on the skyline. The darkness of the mass became lead coloured and then green with light and dark shades and after that I saw a densely wooded mountainous island. Someone said it was Guadalcanal. This was not a sunlit South Sea Island of romantic fiction: it inspired me with a faint melancholy as I gazed at it.

More islands appeared as we steamed on, hilly, wooded, shrouded in mist under a threatening sky. We berthed at tea-time, and immense purple and blue-black clouds piled up and a strange light presaged storm.

Tulagi was a small island. The wooden buildings we could see on the waterside, I was told, were the hospital, prison and offices. Houses where officials lived—white painted, red roofed and easily seen against the greenery of the island—were scattered about on the sharply rising wooded land behind. The highest and biggest of them was the Residency, with a sentry box, flagstaff and Union Jack.

The Boarding Officer brought me a message that I was to see the Resident Commissioner at nine o'clock next morning. I supposed that Anderson had been told the same. Nothing was said about arrangements for landing until one of the passengers named Melhuish hurried along the deck to me.

2

"I'm going ashore," he said. "You dine on board and I'll fetch you at half-past nine."

Men in badly tailored tropical clothes came up the gangway, planters and traders meeting the ship for mail and cargo, men off schooners and inter-island ships, junior government officials and out-of-works off the beach. They greeted the stewards boisterously and then sat round the smoking-room tables to drink.

Just before sunset, lightning flashed across the sky and there was a clap of thunder like high explosive. Then rain fell in torrents. Anderson joined me and we regarded the deluge with wonder.

After dinner the storm abated, but light rain continued to fall. We sat on chairs on the top deck outside our cabin, preoccupied and with nothing to say. I looked round at the sound of steps on the deck.

I saw a man of about forty, slimly built with close-set sallow features and dark well-brushed hair. His linen suit was well cut and he wore a club tie. His manner was jaunty.

"Good-evening," he said brightly, "Anderson, Fowler?" We stood up. "Sit down, sit down," he begged us. "If you don't mind, I'll join you. I'm Brayne. I've been in Tulagi helping Mr Darcy. I leave for Malaita next week. I was hoping to find you and I thought you might be here. The smoking-room on steamer night in Tulagi is to be avoided."

He talked well and we listened with interest to what he told us about the islands. Then he gave us advice.

"I've amused myself learning some of the languages," he said. "I advise you to try it—just for a rag, don't you know, just for a rag."

There were more steps on the deck. Brayne introduced the newcomer as Rae, from Guadalcanal.

"It's no use doing that," Brayne said when I got up to press the bell in our cabin. "No one will come."

"I'll go down to the smoking-room then," I said. "I must at least get cigarettes."

Downstairs on the lower deck the drone of the auxiliary engine was louder. Though the rain had stopped, the ship was damp and felt close and humid. The smoking-room was crowded and hot, and the uproar in the place was stunning. The whirring ceiling fan sent smoke away in eddies but brought no relief. I got my cigarettes at the service hatch, and the barman gave me my change. As I turned to go, a gross giant of a man shuffled towards me. His paunch sagged over his belt and his shirt gaped open to his navel. He looked me up and down with affected surprise. "Well, for God's sake, look who's here," he declared in a melodious deep bass voice. Then, as though amused by what he saw, he tapped my shoulder and bringing his face close to mine he whispered, "She hadn't up to yesterday, pal, but I know she will tonight." I could smell the stale sweat on him and I felt crowded by his bulk. There was laughter, but someone shouted above the din, "Sit down, Hector." The drunken man looked back at me reluctantly as he rejoined his companions.

Rae was on the companion-way talking to a fair-haired man who was holding himself up by the handrail. "You join the police," Rae was saying to him good humouredly, "you'd make a monstrous policeman."

Melhuish was waiting for me with Brayne and Anderson.

It was cool in the launch as we crossed the harbour to the Government Wharf where Melhuish and I picked our way between puddles by the light of Melhuish's torch and took a coral-gravel path which zigzagged up the hillside. For the first time I heard the *tchik tchik* of cicadas and saw the flickering sparkle of fireflies. Lamp light showed dimly from houses set back from the path, and in the gloom we caught the heady scent of night flowering blooms. The lights of the *Mataram* across the harbour at Burns Philp Wharf flattered the ship, suggesting luxury and space.

"I'm seeing the Resident Commissioner tomorrow at nine o'clock," I told Melhuish as we walked slowly up the hill.

"I've not met him," Melhuish said. "He's new."

"I wish my helmet hadn't got so dirty in Colombo," I said; "first impressions are so important."

"He needn't see your helmet; you'll take it off before you go into his office."

"I wish it was clean all the same," I said. "He may notice it."

Melhuish said nothing. The path now ran along a ridge and we walked on in silence. Then Melhuish stopped at a narrow side path with an overgrown hedge. "This is it," he said. I followed him along a few yards of gravel and up two steps into the house.

There was a verandah and four small rooms. In one of them an oil lamp stood on a table. Melhuish turned up the wick and flooded the barely furnished room with yellow light, revealing ferns and plants in tubs on the verandah. I sat down in a wicker chair. I was tired and depressed. Melhuish put a match to his pipe.

"Do you know a big man with dark hair called Hector?" I asked.

"A sallow man with a big mouth?"

"Yes."

"Sounds like Hector Pratt."

"What does he do?"

"He's got a schooner and does a bit of recruiting and sometimes picks up copra."

I told Melhuish what had happened in the smoking-room when I went for cigarettes.

"That's Pratt," he said. "He's a loud-mouthed bully."

We sat a little longer, not saying much; and then Melhuish stood up and knocked his pipe out.

"I think we might as well turn in. What do you say?"

"Yes, I am all for it," I said.

He took me to one of the rooms. A bed was made up, and a mosquito net tucked under the mattress hung down from a frame.

"You'll be all right here. Good-night."

"Good-night," I said.

The pillow was musty and the mattress was hard, but almost

immediately I fell into a deep sleep, untroubled by the doubts and disappointments of the day. It was daylight when I awoke, and the sun was shining. I put on slippers and went out. Melhuish was in the pantry cleaning my helmet. I turned before he saw me and walked on to the front verandah. I was entranced by what I saw and went down the steps into the garden. There were hibiscus bushes with scarlet, white and apricot coloured flowers. Frangipani trees with funereal cream-and-white blooms gave off a cloying scent. On a tree at the end of the garden a purple orchid was in full flower. Then I noticed the *poinciana regia,* the flame tree, at the edge of the path outside, a gorgeous medley of red and yellow. Down the slope below the house, three hornbills, with black wings and white tails, flew laboriously with raucous staccato cries and whirring wings to a clump of trees. Farther away a flock of cockatoos, frightened by something, screeched noisily. I walked round the garden. At the top of a coconut palm two red parrots clung upside down pecking at flowers. A crimson pygmy parrot perched on one of the hibiscus bushes; it flew off to the end of the garden and then a remarkable butterfly appeared. Its colouring was of rare beauty, but I marvelled most at its size. It must have measured seven or eight inches across its open wings. I went back into the house. Melhuish had dressed and looked fresh and cool in white drill trousers and an open-neck shirt.

"This is a wonderful place!" I exclaimed. "I have just seen an enormous butterfly. It was as big as a bird."

Melhuish smiled. "You feel better about Tulagi today?"

"What?—its a marvellous place, absolutely marvellous, it really is," I declared.

I walked to the Residency just before nine o'clock. The water in the harbour, showing shallows and depths by variegated shades of blue and green, lay placid and still. Small craft rode at anchor; two launches crossing to the Government Wharf left a wake of white froth. Over at Burns Philp Wharf winches were at work discharging the *Mataram's* cargo before she started her round of the islands to fill up with copra.

6

The Residency stood on a hillock at the highest point of the island. A grassy bank sloped down to a bed of bronze-leafed cannas, showy plants with large scarlet blooms which made a gaudy display in the bright morning sun. I climbed the cement steps to the house. Anderson had already arrived and was waiting on the verandah. He was well dressed and looked self-possessed.

Darcy, the Resident Commissioner, came out of his room and greeted us. He was a good-looking dark-haired man, slightly above average height, compactly built and with an unmistakable air of authority. He saw Anderson first, and gave me a book to read while I waited.

Anderson came out, still self-possessed and, I thought, smiling slightly. He told me to go in. Prints of officers of the Peninsular campaign hung round the room and there were some team groups. A hide cricket-bag lay on the floor against a wall; a bag of golf clubs stood in a corner with two tennis-rackets in an outsize press. Brayne sat with Darcy behind the desk. He held his head at a tilt and he had an air of being attentive and interested. Darcy pushed a silver cigarette-box towards me. He was not entirely at ease. He told me that Anderson was going out to a district. I was to remain in Tulagi attached to his office for a time, then I would go to the Treasury and later on to the Police and Prison.

The Resident Commissioner's office was near the Residency and looked down over the harbour. A central space separated the offices of Darcy and his typist from those of the Secretary and the Chief Magistrate which were at the other end of the building; but both these rooms were empty. Hever the clerk, pale and ill looking, sat at a table in the middle of the central room facing the main entrance.

Darcy sometimes called me to his office and showed me a file; he even asked my opinion occasionally. I sat with him in court when he acted as judge; and he did his best to find me trifling tasks, but there were many days when I was idle. I made friends with Hever. Jones, the middle-aged typist, regarded me with dislike until one morning, when Darcy was away, I walked into his room when he was cleaning his machine. He grunted when he saw me and went on with his work; but when I admired some sheets of his typescript he was pleased.

"It'll do yer, eh?" he enquired.

"It's beautiful typing," I assured him.

He put down his brush and wiped the machine with a rag. He took a cigarette and gave one to me. He spoke caustically about people in Tulagi and made me laugh.

"See that?" he asked pointing to a crack in the board partition.

"Yes."

"I can hear every word he says through that."

"Do you listen much?"

"Yes. I listen quite a bit; depends who's in there of course. Have a beer?"

I laughed. "Not for me, thanks. It's too early."

"Too early, why?" Jones asked, as he turned and took a bottle from behind a cupboard.

"I had breakfast only half an hour ago," I said.

"I've had no breakfast."

He poured out beer for himself. "There's only one glass anyway," he said. He gulped the beer and took a scrap of paper from his table. 'Two cold ones,' he wrote, and signed his name. He gave the note to a messenger, who went off without a word.

"Where d'you send that?" I asked.

"To Charlie Koenig in Chinatown."

Hever peered through the open doorway.

"Don't let Jones teach you bad habits," he said.

Jones turned on him furiously, and Hever smiled sadly and returned to his table.

The days passed. I sat in the Chief Magistrate's room helping Darcy when I could, gossiping with Hever and Jones and staring down at the harbour. One morning a large schooner moved slowly up the harbour under its auxiliary engine. It anchored away from the usual schooner berths. An hour later

a young American came to the office. He said he was Hamilton
Hamlin of Salem, Massachusetts, and that he had just come from
the Marquesas. He stopped and talked to us, and afterwards,
when he came out of Darcy's room, he invited me to look over
the schooner. The next day Hever said that Darcy was not
coming to the office, so I went down to the waterside and
hailed Hamlin. An immensely muscled Tahitian sculled a
dinghy to the coral stones where I was standing and took me
off to the schooner.

"Come aboard," Hamlin said, "it's good to see you; Mr
Darcy will be here soon and I guess we'll have some coffee."

"Put me ashore," I said to Hamlin, but I was too late. Darcy
in a white topee and palm-beach suit was standing on the coral
stones and the Tahitian was sculling the dinghy towards him.

"Put me ashore," I repeated urgently.

"Sure, sure," Hamlin said, taking in the situation. He called
to one of the crew to bring another boat round to the side. I
passed Darcy half-way between the schooner and the shore. He
said nothing and made no sign of having seen me, but next
morning Hever said he wanted to speak to me.

"Sit down, Fowler," he said offering me a cigarette. "I had
planned to keep you in Tulagi for another month, but I don't
think you are doing much good here. No one has time to teach
you anything. Barrington at Ysabel wants to go on leave; I've
decided you shall relieve him. Hever will arrange details and
tell Barrington when to expect you." He stood up and walked
with me to the door, giving me a friendly pat on the shoulder.
"I'll come and see you soon after you've taken over Ysabel.
You'll dine with us the night before you leave." He smiled and
closed the door after me.

In November 1567 Alvaro de Mendaña set sail with two
ships from the port of Callao in Peru. Three months later they
came to a thickly wooded mountainous island about a hundred
and twenty-five miles long and fifteen miles wide. Mendaña
named it Ysabel in honour of his wife. He discovered many
more islands in nearby waters, some long, mountainous and

9

wooded like his first discovery, others small, bare and rocky. He left in August 1568 and after much hardship reached Peru in 1569. He named his discoveries the Islas de Salomon, boasting that from them came the gold of King Solomon's temple. There was a second expedition in 1595, but Mendaña never saw the islands again, and as the account of his first voyage was lost for many years people began to speak of the Solomon Islands as mythical. They were rediscovered two centuries later by Captain Carteret of the British Royal Navy and given the names that Mendaña had recorded in his account. It was to the island of Ysabel which he had named after his wife that I was posted. It had no other name, though it was often called Bugotu after the southern end of the island.

The *Hygeia* was a fifty-foot-long launch driven by a diesel engine with an exhaust pipe pointing upwards like a narrow smoke-stack. There was a chart house and a permanent wooden awning on deck, and below were the engine room and cabin. She was not a good-looking craft; her excessive top hamper was unsightly, but in a calm sea she was comfortable and fast. Hever arranged for her to take me to Ysabel. Bandy Coot, a much travelled but improvident Cockney, was her engineer-navigator. He was barely literate, but he was skilful with engines and understood ships. Young administrative officers made him testy and irritable. He was suspicious and never sure whether they were treating him with proper respect. He showed no pleasure when I went aboard at the Government Wharf to ask when we would leave.

Coot delayed departure for more than an hour after the time he had appointed. About the middle of the afternoon he took the wheel in the chart house, signalled the engine room and steered the *Hygeia* out of the harbour. I looked back at Tulagi, at the Residency on the hill and at the office, at the red-roofed house I had shared with Melhuish and at the other houses —the treasury and the offices on the waterside, the prison and the hospital buildings. When we were clear of Tulagi, Coot came aft where I was sitting in a canvas chair. The *Hygeia* was on a north-west course along the coast of Gela. The air was languid and the sea still and hazy.

"You get these calms in the north-west season," he said indifferently, looking at the sea. "They're all right for us, but they'd be a bugger if you had only sail."

"Yes, I suppose they would be," I said.

He said no more and went for'ard again to the chart house. When he came back he sat down and began plaiting string and covering the clapper of a small ship's bell. I watched him in silence for a few minutes.

"That's very clever," I said.

"Not many people can do it. It's only the old timers who've been in sail who know how."

"How do you come to be able to do it?"

"Ole Petersen showed me."

I watched him for a time and then looked out at the land. Sharp peaks, rounded hills, grassy tracts on the thickly wooded slopes, clusters of huts and a few canoes gave the scene agreeable variety. We had tea, and then Coot put away the bell and became busy about the ship, moving from engine room to chart house, speaking abusively to the crew and staring straight ahead. Off the end of Gela he pointed to an island. "That's Olevuga," he said. "It's shaped like a big anchor." Later a second island came into sight. "That's Buena Vista. You'll feel the tide rip between the two islands. It's strong here." He went for'ard again and the *Hygeia* rolled sharply as we passed through the channel. Buena Vista was shaped like a horseshoe. Coot took the *Hygeia* across the opening, round the reef and through a passage to enclosed water between the reef and the beach. We anchored just before dusk as the sun had begun to set.

Coot was relaxed and sat with me smoking and sipping whisky until it was dark and hurricane lamps were lit and we had food on a folding table where we sat. My boy Atiu brought up a mattress from the cabin and made up a bed for me on the engine-room housing and I settled myself to read. Coot went for'ard to a camp bed in the chart house. "Dowse the glim when you're finished," he said.

We left Buena Vista at daylight and the *Hygeia* went on as steady as a house through a dead calm sea. After breakfast I went for'ard and stood with Coot in the chart house.

"See that?" he asked.

I peered into the haze but saw nothing but the shimmering sunlight on the water.

"What?" I asked.

"That rock."

Then I saw it—like a great monolith standing in isolation in the middle of the sea.

"Yes, I can see it now; it's extraordinary."

"That's Rua Dika; it's over fifty foot high. There's shoal water near it and I always keep about a mile to the north-west when I am passing it. When we get beyond here I reckon we're half-way between Buena Vista and the south-east end of Ysabel."

"How far is Ysabel after that?" I asked.

"About ten mile to the island and another ten or twelve to Tataba. You'll see the mountains soon."

He was right; just after we passed Rua Dika I saw in the distance the greenish grey outline of high land.

"That's Cape Prieto. It sticks a long way out."

The glare of the sun on the water made my eyes ache and I went back to my chair aft and read for an hour. When I came for'ard again I saw a rocky cliff at the point of Cape Prieto with steeply rising hills behind it, clothed in dense forests. Half an hour later we were off the end of Ysabel, and Coot steered a course between the mainland and a succession of islands on our starboard side. One island might have been half a mile long, but most of them were small, some no more than tiny islets, picturesque, with two or three coconut palms spraying out over the sea.

"Charts don't help here," Coot said abruptly. "You got to know where the reefs are."

"I suppose you have," I said.

"Sometimes you get a strong tide running here," he said, staring ahead intently as he spoke.

I suddenly wondered if I was a distraction to him. I went aft and read spasmodically, sometimes looking at the passing coastline and sometimes dozing. I started slightly when Coot came out of the chart house and shouted at me.

"If you come for'ard you can see your house."

I joined him and stared ahead. In the distance there was the opening to a large harbour. On the west side of it a patch of bare hillside stretched down to the sea, and on the east side there was a small rocky point.

"That's Tataba," Coot said.

For a moment my feelings were tumultuous, and I felt a quickening heart beat.

"How small it seems," I said. "It just looks as though a bit of bush had been scraped away."

"You'll find it quite big."

"Where's the house?"

"Right at the top of the hill on the edge of the bush."

"I can't see it,"

"Take these," he said, handing me his glasses.

I focused the glasses and a picture came into view of a small white house with a red roof at the top of the hill. Behind the house was a very big tree.

"Is that the house with the big tree behind it?" I asked.

"Yes, some people steer on that tree."

"I can see the flagstaff now and a hut lower down the hill on the point."

"You mean the office?"

"The office—that native hut?"

"Yes, sure: it's all right."

"Good heavens!" I exclaimed. "There are some more huts just above the beach."

"Yes, those are the police barracks and all that."

I handed the glasses back to him. I could think of nothing to say.

Coot gave an order to the helmsman in the bad-tempered manner he used to his crew.

The ship began to swing round. "We go a bit to the north-

13

west to get round the first reef and then we come right back to the south-east to get round the second one. The harbour's got a narrow entrance."

There were natives on the beach near the huts, and then as we made the sweep outside the marking buoys on the inner reef I saw a white man walking hurriedly down the path from the house.

"The best thing about Tataba is at the end of that wharf," Coot declared.

A cutter-rigged vessel was moored there, inside the harbour.

"That ship?" I asked.

"Yes, that's the *Wai-ai*, the finest ship of her size in the Solomons."

"I'm glad to hear that," I said. "What does her name mean?"

"It's a place down in San Cristoval in the Eastern Solomons."

Coot now repeatedly telegraphed to the engine room, and he brought the *Hygeia*, barely moving, alongside the *Wai-ai*. I clambered out across the deck to the wharf. A man in khaki slacks, a white shirt and an old felt hat was waiting there. He was big and well set up; he had a grizzled moustache and keen grey blue eyes, a distinguished, genial-looking man. He smiled and came forward. "Fowler?" he asked. "I'm Barrington." Coot did not come ashore; he said he wanted to turn round immediately for Tulagi as soon as my baggage was off-loaded.

I walked with Barrington along the coral stone pier to a path up the hillside. It was a sharp climb to the flat grassy expanse where we halted.

"This is Draper Point where we are standing," Barrington told me. "It's the western entrance point of the harbour. Over there, with the two pinnacle rocks just to the east of it, is Martin Point, the eastern entrance point. Here's your office." It was the native building I had seen from the *Hygeia*. The palm thatch roof was thick, but looked weathered. The walls were strengthened by split bamboos laid against the outside and held in place by rough-hewn vertical laths. Door and window frames in rough joinery fitted into the leaf-and-bamboo walls. "You'll know it well enough before long," Barrington said, "but you might care to look inside before we go up to the house." A side door gave on to a wide entrance passage with a floor of beaten earth; there were two rooms. The main room was the office; and here the floor was covered by a lattice work of split, interlaced bamboo. There were two tables; a Remington typewriter stood on one and on the other there was a trough book-shelf of dog-eared law books, a blotter, a bottle of ink and a pen and pencil. A safe raised up on a stand stood in a corner. "It's very primitive, but you'll get used to it," Barrington said. "I keep the stationery, court forms, letters and so on in here," he added looking at a cupboard. "What are these?" I asked, pointing at two stout wooden boxes. "Travelling boxes," he said. "You take them on tour for money, receipt books, court records and the rest of it."

We walked back into the passage. Barrington stopped. "I've got a carpenter's bench in here," he said at the entrance to the second room.

"What's that for?"

"I go in there and work sometimes."

"What sort of work?"

"Oh, I make things for something to do."

"In office hours?"

Barrington laughed. "Oh yes, in office hours," he said.

The hum of the *Hygeia's* engine carried up from the harbour. Coot had turned round without delay on his way back to Tulagi.

"The view is better from the house, but you can see a lot from here," Barrington said as we came out of the office. "The harbour is about two and half miles across at its widest, and there is a branch which you can't see which runs in for about two miles."

The wide expanse of still water was almost landlocked by densely wooded hills, now partly shrouded by a thin veil of mist. Straight across the water there were two peaks joined as though by a high pass.

"Does that go anywhere special?" I asked Barrington, pointing at the gap between the peaks.

"There is a climb up there, then you drop down on the other side to the sea near Burutu, the mission place. It's like crossing a peninsula. Instead of going all the way round Cape Prieto by sea, you can cross the harbour by canoe and climb over the hills. That's the way you'll get your mail."

"How do you mean?"

"Petrie who's got a trade store at Loga Point on the other side of the island, will drop your mail at Burutu every six weeks. A couple of constables take a canoe across the water and then go on by foot to the other side and bring the mail back."

An imperceptible movement of the sea and the faintest line of froth revealed the coastal reef. Beyond, the sea stretched away blue green to the horizon, glinting here and there in the bright sun. To the north-west a bay swept into the coastline almost from where we were standing to a headland four or five miles away which lay pointing out to sea like the long snout of a crocodile.

"That's Fulakora Point," Barrington said. "If you have got a line out you will nearly always catch a fish there on the way up the coast."

We left the grassy precincts of the office and made our way up a second hill. The path ran along a ridge and on either side red clayey earth sloped away, scoured into channels by heavy rain.

The house stood at the top of the hill and behind it the land dipped down before it rose again steadily to the high wooded mountain range that ran the length of the island. The house was painted white and was raised on tarred hardwood piles. It contained four small rooms, with a wide verandah back and front. There was a patch of poor lawn in front, two stunted frangipani trees, a few hibiscus bushes, and the flagstaff from which the Union Jack hung limply in the still air. There was another patch of lawn on one side, and on the other a kitchen garden. A path led to an earth closet behind the house.

"We might have a drink; what will you have?" Barrington asked when he had shown me the house. We sat in light wicker chairs in the end room gazing through the window at the sea beyond the reef.

"I'd like a squash," I said.

"Quite right, that's what I have at this time of day, but I think today we ought to have a bottle of beer each."

"That would be very nice," I agreed.

He went out and returned with two bottles of beer.

"This is Bulimba beer; it is brewed in Queensland, or is it Tasmania?" He held a bottle away from him, trying to read the label. "I can't see, but it is very good."

Barrington opened the bottles and poured out two tankards. He put a full tankard and a half-empty bottle of beer on a stool at my side. "Good health," he said. I drank the beer slowly. "Good health," I replied.

Neither of us spoke for several minutes.

"How old are you?" Barrington suddenly demanded.

"I'm twenty-two," I said.

"Twenty-two!" he repeated.

"Yes."

"Dear me, I was in these islands before you were born.'

He stared at me without speaking and then, as though putting his thoughts into words, he asked, "What made you come here?"

"I don't know," I said. "I seemed to get caught up in something and went on with it. I think really it was curiosity as much as anything."

"You didn't come out here with any ideas about doing good, or anything like that?"

"No, I had no ideas like that."

"That's good," he said, as though relieved.

I was embarrassed by the turn the conversation had taken.

"Do you speak the language?" I asked him.

"What language?"

"The language of the people here."

"There are at least six different languages spoken in this island."

"Six languages!" I exclaimed.

"Yes, but you could probably make yourself understood in

17

most parts with Bugotu—the language they speak at the south-east end of the island," Barrington said.

"Is Bugotu difficult to learn?" I asked.

"I don't know, I've never tried."

He took a swig of beer and regarded me contemplatively.

"I shouldn't worry about languages," he said. "After a lot of trouble you might learn one which would help you a little but it would be useless if you were transferred to Malaita, Guadalcanal, San Cristoval, or to the Western Solomons."

"This chap Brayne, who met Anderson and me when we arrived, advised us to learn a language."

"Ah yes, Brayne, he's got a gift; he learns languages easily. But if you are like me you'll find it hard work. Are you good at languages?"

"No."

"Well, don't waste time on them."

"I'll see how I get on," I said.

A boy of about seventeen in a white *lava lava* came silently barefoot into the room. "*Kai kai* ready," he said. "Take your beer with you," Barrington told me as he rose from his chair.

We rested during the afternoon and after tea as we went down the back steps I admired the big banyan tree. It was an enormous, spreading, smooth-barked tree with large leathery shiny leaves. Aerial roots hanging down from the branches to the ground had developed as though into independent trunks supporting one immense head.

"I'm glad they didn't cut that down," I said.

"They couldn't; the tree's mentioned in Admiralty Sailing Directions, though I must say there have been times when I wished it wasn't here," Barrington said.

"Why?"

"Flying foxes roost there and squeak at night, and I think it harbours snakes. Besides, the local people are scared of it. You won't get anyone to come here after dark."

"What are they scared about?"

"They believe the tree is haunted."

"Haunted?"

"Yes, that's what they say. Years ago there used to be a hut here where the women came to have their babies. There was a chief's wife who came and died in great agony. They say she was an unrepentant adulteress, and now she haunts this tree."

We walked down the path towards the office. About half-way, forty or fifty yards from the path, there was a large hut.

"We might have a look at the prison," Barrington said.

Prisoners were sitting outside the hut in their broad-arrow marked *lava lavas*, eating rice and talking noisily.

"They seem very cheerful," I said.

"Yes, there ought to be a high fence round the building and a strong gate and all the rest of it."

"How many prisoners are there as a rule?"

"Seldom more than a dozen—on an average six or seven in at one time, I suppose."

"Do they ever escape?"

"Sometimes, but most of them like it here and don't want to leave."

We went back to the main path and walked on to the office. Two paths sloped down, one on each side of the point. We took the left-hand one, which brought us to the beach. A croton-hedged path, with towering coconut palms leaning out from it to the sea, went away in the distance.

"This joins a bush track which goes on to the village of Regi about two miles away," Barrington said.

On the flat land between the beach and the rise of the ridge there was a long, well-made native building, raised a few feet off the ground.

Three muscular young men sitting on the verandah stood up at our approach and immediately afterwards an older man came out. He was short, not much over five feet four, but he had a trim powerful build and he looked at us with an un-wavering gaze. "Corporal Dolimae," Barrington said, "this is Mr Fowler, who will be your new master." Dolimae turned his gaze on me and saluted. I mumbled a greeting and said that I expected he would help me in my work, and then Barrington dismissed him and we walked on.

After supper that evening we sat in the sitting-room and Barrington talked about the district. Suddenly someone began beating a hollow log drum. There was verve and spontaneity in the rolls and variations; it was an agreeable, arresting sound.

"What's that?" I asked.

"It's one of the police preparing to beat out nine o'clock. On fine nights some of them go on for ten minutes. I like hearing it."

Next morning I went down to the office with Barrington. A constable saluted us at the door. Even among people where good physique was common, this man was exceptional. He was not big, but the muscles of his arms, chest and back were beautifully formed. When he moved, his *lava lava* stretched tightly against his thighs. He was about my age.

"This is Hiro," Barrington said. "He sits at that table out in the passage-way and acts as my orderly. I've depended on him a lot in the past two years."

"He can do the same thing for me," I said.

I checked the account books and counted the cash and Barrington gave me the key of the safe. I saw the police kit, rifles and ammunition. I counted the bags of rice, tins of meat, cases of ship's biscuits and the rest of the food in the ration store. We walked by the path round the rocks in front of Draper Point to the *Wai-ai*, where the crew had laid out the ship's stores on the wharf. There was Kepi the bo'sun, a light-coloured, chalky-complexioned man with large luminous eyes, Soge the engine man, smaller but with a sharp intelligent face, and the two deck hands, younger men, Gagi and Wesu. I looked at lengths of canvas, rope, pulley blocks, sewing palms, marline spikes and other gear. We then went up to the office and verified the prisoners' warrants.

I walked down to the wharf to see Barrington off.

"What are you going to do when I've gone?" he asked me.

"I'll check over the office again to make it foolproof," I said.

"Oh yes, how will you do that?"

Ysabel

"Just look at everything to make sure its correct."

"I see; what a splendid idea."

"I'll go up the coast after that and call at some of the villages."

"You'll enjoy that."

We walked along the wharf to the *Wai-ai*. "The best of luck to you," Barrington said when we got to the ship, "and take a bit of advice from me—don't stay too long in these islands." He shook my hand and stepped aboard. I remained at the end of the wharf watching the ship as she passed out of sight behind Draper Point before coming back round the outer reef on the course for Tulagi. I walked quickly up the hill to the office and watched the ship again until the sound of her engine grew fainter and she disappeared beyond Martin Point. I turned and entered the office and sat down at the table, suddenly overwhelmed by want of confidence in myself. I was now responsible for the peace, good order and government of a large island and its thousands of inhabitants. Barrington with his wisdom and experience, made the task sound easy, but he had gone and I was alone. I felt ill-prepared for the charges which had been thrust upon me. I got up and walked over the springy bamboo floor-covering. I opened the safe and looked at the bundles of notes and the *rouleaux* of shillings I had taken over. I plaited lengths of tape, tied them to the key and then threaded them through a belt loop on my trousers. I wandered round the room opening and closing cupboards and looking at old law books. I picked up and examined three rusted shotguns which stood in a corner. Then I went outside to the passage where Hiro sat and looked at the medicines and bandages on the shelves there. I inspected the room where Barrington had had his carpenter's bench. It could be made into a court room, I thought. When I went back into the office, a large crab crawled awkwardly over the bamboo strips—it was a robber crab which had cast up earth like a mole behind Hiro's chair.

I left the office at noon and walked up to the house. I had taken on Barrington's boy, Beni, as cook. He could bake bread and make white sauce. He and Atiu made an ill-assorted pair of servants.

21

CHAPTER TWO

The Missionary

AT eight o'clock Corporal Dolimae came into the office and stood at attention facing me across the table. He saluted, brought his hand down with a slap on his thigh and reported.

"Everyt'ing arright along night," he stated. "Eight fella police stop arright; Constable Hiro go along Tulagi; seven fella prisoner he stop arright; warder he stop arright; fifty-seven fowl and nine fella duck he stop arright; four fella cow he stop arright. Wind he come for one o'clock; rain he come for two o'clock. *Wai-ai* no come back from Tulagi. Everyt'ing stop arright along night," he concluded decisively. He regarded me with fixed unwavering eyes. I looked back at him uncertain what to say. I moved my eyes to the wirey black hairs on his chest and back to his face again. "Thank you, corporal," I said finally. He saluted again, smacked his thigh, turned to the left and marched out.

The sea shimmered in the morning haze and there was no wind; it was the start of another hot day. I went down to the beach, round Draper Point and along to the end of the wharf. I watched fish swimming in the placid water below and slowly returned. Prisoners sweeping leaves on the path to the office made way when I reached them. I talked to the warder and went on to the office. I had been out twenty minutes. I opened a law book, but closed it again at a sound in the passage. A constable appeared.

"Who are you?" I asked.

"Constable Hoile, sir," he said saluting. "Corporal say tell you Walter Notere come."

Barrington had been guarded in speaking about Notere. People in Tulagi had told me more. Traders spoke of him with a laugh.

"Walter, he's a bloody rogue all right; you want to watch him," they said, and then, lest I might be cast down by their criticism, they were apt to add, "but I like the old bastard, you can't help liking him."

He had other critics. He was barred from the church fellowship on Ysabel; he was regarded as evil.

"Tell him come in," I said.

Notere was a man of sixty-five to seventy with white hair and a lined cadaverous face, a knowing shrewd-looking man. The sneers of traders and the slander of enemies had done nothing to impair his dignified bearing and easy manner. I stood up and held out my hand.

"I'm glad to see you," I said.

"I am glad too much to see you," he replied. "I was at Vulavu when I hear you come to Tataba; I no go for my place at Furona, I come here to report."

He wore a black sateen *lava lava* with a vest and a white cardigan. A silk handkerchief was knotted round his neck. As badges of office he wore a red sash and a heavy leather belt. Obsolete uniform belts were sold by island traders. On the polished buckle of Notere's belt were the words 'The City of Glasgow Fire Brigade'.

I asked him about tax payment.

"The price of copra is low now; the traders only give six shillings a bag—a year ago they gave a pound. There is not much money in copra today."

"I see the Chinamen's schooners going up the coast, they must do some trading."

"That's true, master. Young men dive for trochus shell and sell it to Chinamen and white men and get some money. But there are people who can't dive—bushmen and old men. Some can make canoes and build houses; some can sell tobacco leaf or work the garden of another man. Money from trochus shell gets about that way, but it takes time. In three months we can ask people to pay."

24

Island trade in shell was an old thing. In the early days gold lip shell was sold, a large flat bivalve, a beautiful lustrous thing inside. Black lip shell was smaller and the pearly inside coating had a silvery hue. Green snail shell was a substitute for jade. Perhaps these shells lay at a great depth or perhaps nearby reefs had been stripped of them; trade now seemed only in trochus shell, a small conical shell about three inches long.

"Is there plenty of shell on the reefs?" I asked.

Notere looked concerned at my question and replied emphatically.

"No, there is not; there's been too much diving."

"But there's a reef off every coastal village. Can't the headmen stop too much diving?"

"Once they could make a reef *tabu*, but it doesn't always work today. Sometimes a Chinaman or a white man brings a schooner and orders his crew to dive for shell. That's the way the reef gets spoiled."

Notere's detractors might have spoken less evil of him had they known how much he emphasised the difficulties of his people and how constantly he sought their good.

Nobody else came to see me that day, and when I returned to the office in the afternoon I sat idly until four o'clock and then the old habit of exercise asserted itself. In shorts and tennis-shoes I walked smartly down the hill to the beach. The croton-hedged path above the sea-wrack on the coral shingle went into the bush at the station boundary. There had been no recent rain and the carpet of leaves was dry. Someone had killed a monitor lizard and a swarm of flies buzzed round its mutilated body. Sweat poured down my face as I strode quickly along the sheltered path. Bread fruit trees stood in a clump on the outskirts of the village and the path widened at a grove of areca palms and I saw the first huts. I drove off two ferociously barking dogs and walked into the village. Blue wood smoke curled up from open fires and the smell of cooking fish hung heavily in the air. Women with hardwood poles pounded food in wooden mortars. I watched a canoe maker fitting together timbers in a framework of lashed sticks and, farther on, two

B

men were thatching a hut with sago palm leaves folded over lengths of cane. A man with a pipe was repairing a fishing net.

The men wore a simple wrapped *lava lava* turned over and tucked in or held up with a belt, but the women's cloth was gathered on a band tied over the hips below the bulge of their soft protuberant stomachs. Children, playing naked on the sandy ground outside the huts, looked at me with wonderment, the youngest of them rushing howling to their mothers as I passed. But no one took much notice of me until a man of sixty or more, stooping a little as he walked, came forward and greeted me.

"Good-afternoon," he said.

"Good-afternoon," I replied.

"My name is Palukue; I am headman of Regi."

"I am glad to see you; I am the new District Officer."

"Oh, good-afternoon," he said again. "If I had known you were coming, I would have met you."

"Where did you learn to speak such good English?" I asked. His face lit up with pleasure.

"You think I speak good English?"

"Yes, very good English."

"I learned at the Kanaka Mission in Queensland."

"In Queensland?"

"Yes, my father and mother were taken to the sugar plantations in 1875."

"That was a long time ago."

He laughed. "Yes, it was a long time ago: I was a small boy then."

I raised my head to listen to a strange sound coming from the bush on our right; it was a repeated tattoo of muffled thuds.

"What's that?" I asked.

"The women are making bark cloth," he said. "They are in the bush behind the coconut grove."

He pointed and I saw smoke rising from a fire beyond the trees.

"They make it for shrouds," he went on.

26

The Missionary

"Can we see them doing it?"

"Of course."

I followed him along the track into the bush. Dirty white material like felt was piled on the ground and seven women squatted on their heels behind a log. Each of them held a square-headed mallet and was beating material spread over the log. Some held the handle of the mallet with one hand, but others took two hands to it. They were all engrossed in their work and paused only to move the material they were beating.

Dark clouds threatened rain; there seemed to be a change in the weather. I shook hands with Palukue and hastened away; two women carrying taro stared at me mouths agape as I passed them on the path. I heard the police skylarking at the barrack, and later when I sat with a book after supper the sound of laughter came up from the beach until the drum sounding ten o'clock brought silence to the station.

As soon as I got to the office next morning someone outside called out with a shrill voice, "Can I come in?" and before I could reply a short slightly-built white man with thin wispy red hair came into the room. I stared at him with surprise—a man of forty or more with an indefinable air of shabbiness about him; not an impressive figure, I thought. He walked slowly towards me with a heavy limp and I saw that his left leg was short and misshapen.

"I'm Woodley from Burutu," he said awkwardly, as though unsure of his welcome.

"Sit down," I said, regarding him with interest, "It's nice to see you."

He hooked his feet round the legs of the chair and regarded me with smouldering uneasy eyes.

"Petrie brought a letter from Barrington for you," he said.

The *Wai-ai*'s engine had failed, Barrington wrote, and the ship had been towed to Tulagi by a Chinaman's schooner. It might be a week before she returned.

"Come up to the house and have lunch," I suggested.

"No, I can't stay for lunch," Woodley replied, "but I'd be glad of a cup of tea."

27

"Where have you come from?" I asked as we walked up the hill.

"From Burutu."

"How did you come round?"

"I didn't come round; I came over the hill and across the harbour by canoe."

"It must be heavy going up that hill."

He giggled. "Missionaries don't travel in the comfort of Government officials."

"There's no merit in discomfort," I retorted. "Where are you going from here?"

"Up the coast."

"By foot and canoe?"

"Of course."

We reached the house and sat near the sitting-room window.

"Walter Notere came to see me yesterday," I said.

Woodley shrugged his shoulders and grimaced.

"Oh, Notere," he said contemptuously.

"What's the matter with Notere?"

Woodley spoke with a sneer.

"He's not a chief at all. You know how he got his position?"

"No."

"They say he used to get women for Blaydon, who was Superintendent of Agriculture years ago."

"Why do you say that? You weren't here then."

"It's true."

I changed the subject. It was obvious that he would have liked to say more.

"Are there other missionaries on the island?" I asked.

"There's a nurse, Miss Thompson, at Huranga Lagoon; what she does I don't know."

There were spots of colour on his high cheek-bones. He was flushed and looked petulant. Conversation had become laboured. I offered him more tea, but he refused it.

"Won't you stay for lunch?" I asked.

"No thank you, no thank you," he said, standing up. "I've been here too long."

The Missionary

I walked with him as far as the office and said I hoped we should soon meet again.

Two weeks later Woodley called again. He allowed me to fill his vacuum flask with hot tea, but refused to stay for a meal. I saw him next when I was touring the villages at the south-east end of the island—villages on the edges of small bays or set back in creeks and anchorages along the coast from Cape Prieto. There was little for me to do there—most of the men were away from home preparing land for yam planting. But when we came to Vulavu, thirty or forty well-built huts above a coral shingle beach, with rising blue smoke drifting away in the wind in the hills behind, I could see many people walking about ashore. The *Wai-ai* was back, and we dropped anchor in coral and sand north of a green rock just off the beach. A man came forward and began talking volubly as soon as the boat was pulled up. Hiro listened impassively.

"What's the matter?" I asked.

"Trouble," said Hiro, listening again as the man spoke with growing vehemence.

"What's the trouble?" I demanded.

Hiro consulted the headman as though removing a doubt.

"There's some trouble about a man and a girl and the people are angry."

"What's the trouble? Is the girl too young or did she not want the man?"

"The girl is not too young; she wanted the man."

The long discussion in the vernacular had irked me and I had become annoyed by the crowd of gaping bystanders.

"Tell these people to go away," I said to Hiro, "and tell the headman to take us to some place where we can talk. I don't understand this business."

The village was at the foot of a craggy thickly wooded hillside. We stood in the shade of a tree near the headman's hut.

"I want to know what is wrong before I see the man and girl," I told Hiro.

"They both belong to the Posomogo line."

29

It was plain that a crime had been committed or at least that there had been a gross outrage of public feeling, but what had caused offence I did not know. The headman was now calmer, as though he had divested himself of responsibility and was waiting upon higher authority to act. I looked from him to Hiro in bewilderment.

"What's this Posomogo line you talk about?" I demanded.

Hiro sighed heavily and wet his lips with his tongue.

"There are three lines," he explained. "Vihuvunagi, Thogokama and Posomogo. In English I think you call them—Eagle, Hawk and Parrot. Everybody belongs to one of these lines. If a man wants a woman, he takes her from another line. A Posomogo man must take a woman from the Vihuvunagi or the Thogokama line. It is very *tabu* for him to take a woman of his own line. Before Government came, if a man and woman of the same line went together, they would be killed. Today the people do not know what to do now that this has happened."

"How can a man know the line of a woman he wants?"

"Everybody in a place knows the line of everybody else. If anyone says he did not know the line of a woman he has taken, he lies."

I turned to the headman.

"Tell the man and girl to come."

The man was about twenty-seven, possibly less, strong, clean and upstanding; but he stood abashed with downcast eyes. He was very frightened. The girl was perhaps sixteen. She had big well-formed breasts and a trim figure. Her face was expressionless; she was less oppressed by guilt than the man.

"What are their names?" I asked.

Hiro consulted the headman.

"Phillip Melema and Alice Loma'a," he replied.

I turned to the man.

"Is what they say about you and this girl true?"

"It is true, master, I can't lie; this girl came to me in the middle of the night, two, three or four times—I'm not sure."

"Is this true?" I asked the girl.

She nodded without any change in her blank expression. "It's true," she said.

The man waited apprehensively for me to speak.

"You understand plantation work?" I asked him.

"I work for ships."

"If I send you to Tulagi, you'll get a job?"

There was disbelief in the look he gave me. Until then I do not think he had pictured anything but degradation as the outcome of his folly.

"I get job," he declared confidently.

"Go to the *Wai-ai*. I'll send you to Tulagi when I get a chance."

He went off without a glance at the girl. The headman nodded with satisfaction when Hiro told him what I had done.

Then I looked at the girl. She stood as though she was not concerned in the arrangements we were making.

"Is this girl ruined now?" I asked the headman.

"No, she is not spoiled for ever."

"She'll get a husband?"

"Yes, some man will want her."

"All right, put her with some woman to work for gardens, house and all the rest of the woman's work. She will learn and have no time to get into more trouble."

As I walked round the village with the headman and Hiro, I saw the girl walking submissively with a woman. A dog barked ferociously at me when they took me to the canoe house, and it became frenzied when one of the men struck at it. A child screamed at me when I gestured at it playfully. I went down to the beach to go off to the *Wai-ai*. It was late afternoon and I wanted some tea.

We took forty minutes to reach the mission island. It was marked Turtle Island on the charts; the native name for it was Finuana, but the mission called it Burutu, after an early native martyr. It was half a mile long by a quarter, a sandy island with some coconut palms and rough scrub. On the eastern side it was almost joined to the mainland by a reef, and there was a second reef running out on the north-west side. On the mainland I saw the conspicuous tree on the saddle between the two hillocks where the police from Tataba came down to Burutu for my mail.

Woodley stood on the rickety wharf waiting for me. He looked at me with sick eyes and his mouth twitched when he spoke. He was unrelaxed and spasmodic in his movements, and as we talked he laughed unnecessarily. When I asked about his health, he said he was well.

The crotons along the path were long and straggling; the place had an air of neglect. The house was small, just three cell-like rooms and a verandah no more than five feet wide. It had been put together with parts brought from Cairns.

Under the eaves and round the window frames there was ornamental fretwork. It looked trivial and incongruous. The original green paint had been a poor choice. It had blistered and flaked, and patches of bare wood showed yellow and brown on the boards. It was a shabby little house and probably hot.

There were two easy chairs, many books, a crucifix on the wall and a prie-dieu in the sitting-room. On a table where Woodley wrote there were six packages all about the same size and shape and there were also four new open-blade razors.

"What are these?" I asked.

"They're razors."

"What, ten of them?"

"Yes, I'm afraid so."

Woodley tittered nervously and seemed embarrassed.

"Where did they all come from?" I asked.

"They were sent from my old parish."

I looked at him with perplexity.

"What do you want ten razors for?" I asked.

"I don't want ten razors," he replied crossly. "It is a mistake. I wrote asking if a kind friend would send me a razor as I couldn't get blades for my Gillette. Ten people sent these razors—there may be even more on the way."

I was mystified; there was something bizarre in having ten brand-new cut-throat razors.

"Why couldn't you get Gillette blades?" I asked. "I use Gillette blades; when I am down to five I send to Tulagi for more."

"Oh for goodness' sake stop talking about the wretched razors," Woodley said shrilly.

Someone in the native-built chapel tolled a cracked bell.

"Will you excuse me, please?" Woodley asked in a more composed voice. "That is Evensong. Sit down; there are some new magazines on the table."

He went into the adjoining room and returned wearing a white cassock and carrying a Prayer Book.

"I won't be long," he said as he took the path to the chapel.

His house-boy and wife would be there, possibly a roust-about who worked outside and maybe a visitor or two. He did not invite me to the service, and for some reason I did not suggest it myself, but when he came back I wished that I had gone.

He asked me to stay to supper. We sat at a folding table and ate tinned sheep-tongues and boiled yams, and then canned apricots and condensed milk. During the meal we drank tea poured from a large pot. Woodley hardly ate anything.

When we had finished, the house-boy took away the table and released a large mosquito net which fell down like a square-sided tent, almost filling the room. It was like sitting in a cage. Woodley filled a pipe, but he was not a habitual smoker and was unable to light it. In response to something Woodley said, the house-boy placed a bottle of whisky and a jug of water on a stool under the net. The smoking and whisky were tokens of good fellowship, but neither of us felt at ease.

I told him about the man and girl at Vulavu.

"Oh yes," he said. "The three clans."

"You know about these things?"

"Oh dear me, yes, of course."

He was patronising, I thought. When I had talked with him

at Tataba there had been at times an acidulous tolerance in his manner.

"These creatures, eagle, hawk and parrot, are clan totems, I suppose?" I said.

"Yes, they are called *tindadho*. Vihuvunagi, the chiefs' clan, has secondary *tindadho*—shark, eel, and so on. People of this clan are not allowed to kill or eat these things. The other two clans have their secondary *tindadho* too."

"I suppose the *tabu* about marriage and intercourse is to prevent inbreeding and weakening the stock?" I said.

I was surprised by the sudden look of pain which came into Woodley's face.

"I don't know anything about that," he said, "but I do know that many people think more of the clan *tabus* than they do of their marriage ties."

"The Church here takes a strong view about sexual morality?"

"It must; what else do you expect it to do?"

"I don't know; avoiding fornication is not of itself particularly meritorious, and by the same token I don't think people ought to be condemned too harshly for an occasional lapse."

I was not prepared for Woodley's extreme distress of mind.

"You don't know what you are talking about," he said. "Last month James Gami went to Lanaga to be examined for the Ministry; I had great hopes for him. The night before the service he seduced a girl at the mission there."

"Poor chap," I said. "He must have got in a muddle."

"Oh dear, dear, dear," Woodley replied. "You speak with great ignorance."

I poured out whisky for myself and made no reply.

"Can I pour you out some of your own whisky?" I asked.

He was abstracted and did not answer at once.

"Yes, all right, but not much," he said shortly when I repeated the question.

It was a brand of whisky I had not seen before.

"Where does this come from?" I asked.

"Friends in Queensland send me a few bottles by the *Jonathan Frost*."

"You lucky man; this is good stuff."

We sat and talked under the net. He told me about his work at home, but I had had a hard day and became too sleepy to listen properly. It seemed late when I pushed up the net to go, but I found it was not nine o'clock when I got back to the *Wai-ai*. There was less noise from the reef on the seaward side of the island; it sounded as though the sea was calm. A land breeze made it cool enough for a light blanket. I fell asleep to the lap lap of water against the ship.

Woodley and I did not meet again for some time. He was away for six weeks at Guadalcanal, and when he returned I was busy on the station for more than a month. The prisoners had begun going off each day with axes cutting posts for the prison fence. There were coils of barbed wire in the ration store and two drums of tar under my house; lime could be made from burning coral on the beach. An enclosed gravelled yard, white lime and tar would help give the hut on the hill the appearance of a prison. I found satisfaction in the simple task of supervising the work, and this and other things kept me agreeably occupied.

There was a labourer on the station named Joe, an old Malaita man who brought me fish and fruit and local vegetables. His legs were short almost to deformity, his head was big and his face with a big expressive mouth and large eyes was comic. The cartilages in his pierced ear-lobes had been enlarged and hung down in loops three inches long. He was a strange looking man, but he went about his work giving offence to no one and he roared with laughter at the playful greeting I usually gave him. I had not seen him for a week. The cheerful grimaces and shouts of laughter which punctuated our dealings had not suggested that he was dissatisfied with the tobacco I gave in exchange for the fish he brought me. I wondered why he had not been to the house when I met him coming up the path from the harbour. He looked bowed down; his grotesque old features were distorted with grief when I stopped to speak

35

to him but I could make nothing of what he said. He was waiting at the office when I got back from my walk and I told Hiro to find out what was troubling him.

"The Regi mission teacher says Joe's wife must leave him," Hiro said.

"Why?" I asked sharply. "What's it got to do with him?"

"They say Reverend Woodley give order."

"Give order! what for?" I demanded. "I don't understand."

"They say Joe has a wife on Malaita."

"Well, that is the business of Joe's woman—if she wants to stay with Joe, that's her affair."

"The mission don't agree."

"All right, what can they do?"

"They stop Joe's woman going to church house with the other women."

"Does she want to go?"

Hiro turned to Joe and spoke partly in his strange pidgin English and partly in Bugotu.

"Joe says nobody at all at Regi talks to his woman now; she cry, cry, cry all day. For a long time three women work in the gardens with Joe's woman and now they are too frightened. Joe thinks his woman will leave him and go back to Regi soon."

I was astonished by what I was told. I thought a grave injustice was being done.

"Is it true Joe had a wife on Malaita?" I asked presently.

"Joe says he left Malaita a long time ago. When he was a young man he had a woman, but he thinks maybe she is dead or taken another man. He doesn't know."

Joe looked less dejected, but I thought it unwise to offer him any hope of relief from trouble.

"How do they know Joe had a wife on Malaita?" I demanded.

Hiro consulted Joe, and then replied.

"Joe told them."

"Until then, they didn't know?"

Hiro shook his head. "Not until Joe told them."

I sat musing while the two men waited for me to speak. I

hoped a solution to the problem would suggest itself. I could think of none.

"Tell Joe to bring his woman here," I said finally.

While we waited for Joe's return, I asked Hiro if he had heard of such things before.

"Yes," he said. "There was a time when no one would speak to a man and woman at Sigosapa; the mission said the woman had another husband. The man became very ill, but nobody helped the woman, and when he died nobody would help to bury him. He began to stink and we police buried him. Master was very cross with the Sigosapa people."

Joe came slowly into the room with the woman. I had often seen her outside Joe's house on the hillside. She looked about fifty. Her breasts hung low, flat like empty pouches; her stomach, distended and flabby, sagged over the band of her cloth. She scratched at her short cropped head as she stared diffidently round the room.

"The woman wants to talk to me?" I asked Hiro.

She was nervous and low spirited and he spoke gently to her.

"This woman does not want to leave Joe," Hiro said. "She has been with him for five years. Two men before him died and now she has no other man but Joe. Joe is good to her; he gives her money to buy calico and tobacco from the Chinese schooner. He makes no trouble at all for her." Hiro consulted the woman and then went on. "She works a small garden for Joe and cooks his *kai kai* for him. Now everyone in the mission says she must leave Joe, but she doesn't want to; she wants to stay with Joe."

I was moved and troubled by what I had heard. Some overzealous catechist may have interpreted a misssion rule too literally, I thought. "Tell them," I said to Hiro, "I don't promise to put this thing right, but I'll try. It is a mission affair."

I did not know whether to write to Woodley or wait until he passed through Tataba on his way up the coast. I decided to wait and not magnify the affair by writing.

Three weeks after my talk with Joe I walked down to the

office after breakfast. Soft fleecy cirrus clouds spreading over the sky gave warning of stormy weather, but the atmosphere, for so early in the morning, was close and still. I found Woodley waiting for me. I was surprised to see him, as I had not had a note to say he was coming. He stood up to greet me and then sat down again and hooked his feet round the legs of the chair. Conversation became spasmodic, and during a lull I broached the subject of Joe.

"I've got a labourer here named Joe," I said.

"Joseph Fakanova of Su'u Malaita?"

"I don't know his full name; he's a Malaita man with a comic face; you must have seen him about."

"I know the man; he's living with Mary Amota."

"That's really what I wanted to speak about."

"Yes?"

"The Regi people are treating Joe's woman badly. They don't allow her to attend church services and no one will speak to her. Even the women of her age-group in her own line who've worked with her for years in the gardens won't speak to her. The woman's distressed, and Joe is too, as he's afraid she'll leave him."

Woodley's eyes smouldered as he waited for me to finish.

I had a presentiment that no good would come of my interference.

"If the woman would leave this man and return to Regi she would be readmitted to the fellowship of the Church."

"You know all about it then?"

"Yes, the facts have been reported to me."

"Do you approve?"

"Certainly. The Church has rules and everyone knows them; people break them at their peril."

"The trouble, I gather, is that Joe admitted that he once had a wife on Malaita."

"As far as I am concerned he still has a wife on Malaita."

"Even though he's not seen her for about twenty years?"

"That makes no difference."

"You don't even know whether the woman is still alive."

"If he can prove his wife is dead, a different view might be taken."

I became speechless with angry bewilderment and then the frustrations of the past weeks found an outlet. I did no good service to Joe or to anyone else when I spoke. "You make me sick," I said. "I'm told your people left a woman with a putrefying corpse and refused to help her. You are all obsessed with sex. You have made marriage too binding and force people into adultery and then persecute them. There used to be an old custom well suited to these people called *doma*; the man was refunded his brideprice and the marriage ended. But you in your great wisdom have stopped that. Why can't you show flexibility instead of encouraging hypocrisy. It is so disgusting. . . ."

Woodley jumped clumsily to his feet and banged the table with both hands. "Silence!" he shrieked in a shrill high-pitched voice. He was too overwrought to articulate properly. "Pray who are you to speak about these things? Why don't you mind your own business?" His voice weakened and he fell silent. He was flushed and trembling violently when he sat down.

I felt nothing but distaste for him.

"Get out of this office," I said.

He stood up, took his haversack and limped out of the room. I sat for several minutes without moving and then went outside. I could see Woodley following the beach path to Regi. He carried a staff and walked with a jerky nervous motion, head held high, looking neither to left nor right. I watched him until he passed out of sight into the bush and immediately I felt remorse. He was ill and I had driven him away instead of giving him a meal or at least hot tea for his vacuum flask.

At the office next morning Hiro made one of his formal requests to speak which so often introduced a tiresome little problem or passed on tittle-tattle about someone on the station.

"What's the matter with you?" I said unwillingly.

He cleared his throat. "Who is number one boss," he asked, "Archbishop of Canterbury or King George?"

I was disturbed less by what he said than by his perception of my train of thought. As I had walked down from the house a few minutes before, disquieting thoughts of conflict between mission and Government had occurred to me. Hiro had often shown a strange prescience, but it never failed to surprise me.

"What did you say?" I asked sharply. He repeated his question and I explained as best I could that the King was head of both State and Church in England, but no one thought of King or Archbishop as being superior one to the other. They worked together, I told him. The King looked to the Archbishop for guidance in religious affairs; the Archbishop depended on the King for the safety of the Church.

"Savvy?" I said when I had finished. "Yes, I understand," Hiro said, but he remained standing at the table and I looked meditatively at him. I suspected that his most important question was yet to come.

"Yes?" I asked at last.

"Every village has a mission headman now," he said.

"Mission headman!"

"Yes, there is one in every place; there is much talk."

"What are the people saying?"

"Some say mission headman is number one in the place and some say Government headman is number one. There is much talk everywhere."

"What do these mission headmen do?"

"Mission work, collect money, make people go the church house, do any small repair for the church house, get canoe for Reverend Woodley or anything he wants. I hear talk that some mission headmen try to do the same as Government headmen and some Government headmen are angry.

"People are asking who is boss—King George or Archbishop?"

"Yes, that's what I hear."

Hiro lingered at the table, but I had heard enough.

"All right," I said, and he went out.

I pondered unhappily over this development. Why could

not Woodley leave well alone, I asked myself. Revival of strife between mission and Government would injure both. I had become aware soon after I reached Tataba of the distrust with which some mission followers looked upon Government. Only a few years had passed since all the affairs of the island had been controlled by the *Vungai Kiloau,* the 'Church Men'. Some of them were sons of chiefs, intelligent and influential men; but they were dictatorial and were scornful of Government headmen. They said these headmen were mission outcasts, people of evil reputation or white men's pimps. Some District Officers had not been blameless; some resisted mission influence and were unfriendly to the teachers, maybe they were misled by their own people who looked to them for a stick to beat a rival. I regretted my impatience with Woodley. With the example of goodwill between us, strife between mission followers and my people would cease. My troubled mind had now found a new cause for worry.

My reconciliation with Woodley took place in strange circumstances. For nearly five months we had avoided each other; he ceased to call at Tataba on his way up the coast, and when I toured the villages at the south-east end of the island I anchored off Burutu only if I were certain he was away from home. I bore him no ill will and I am sure he had no strong dislike for me, but a barrier had come between us which made it difficult for us to meet. There were subjects about which we were bound to disagree and maybe I resented the rival authority he seemed to be setting up on the island. There were times when I was tempted to work off my resentment on the mission headmen I met in the villages, standing aloof with their followers and looking on me with suspicion and sometimes, as it seemed to me, with an air of self-righteous superiority. They knew, and my people knew, of the dissension between Woodley and myself. Tales of obstructing the police were brought to me; lies a lot of the stories were and I had no doubt that Woodley was being fed lies about my police and headmen. These things troubled me. I thought of asking Darcy to suggest to the Field Secretary that Woodley should be moved, then

I thought it better to do nothing and wait until he went on leave. Then, unexpectedly, I found myself in his house at Burutu. I knew I was in his house by the musty smell of vestments, incense and piles of Prayer Books. I opened my eyes and saw the prie-dieu and the crucifix on the wall. I was lying on a camp bed; it was too small and a strut bored into my back. The bed creaked noisily when I moved to find relief. Woodley came into the room wearing a cassock.

"I'm glad to see you awake," he said cheerfully. He took my hand. "Your temperature is down; I think you're better."

"What's the time?" I asked.

"Half-past six; I'm just back from Evensong."

"How long have I been here?"

"Two days. They brought you here the day before yesterday."

"Brought me here?"

"You've been very ill. Your police and crew brought you here. How do you feel now?"

The effort of thought was too much for me. I passed my hand over my face. My chin felt bristly.

"I ought to shave."

"Wait until tomorrow."

"Where's the *Wai-ai*?"

"She's anchored here; do you want to see Hiro?"

"No," I said. "I'd like to sleep."

I waited wearily for him to shake my pillows and straighten the sheets.

"Whose pyjamas are these?" I asked.

"Mine," he said. "They're much too small for you." He put down the net and tucked it in under the mattress. "I'll bring you supper later."

It was dark when he came again and he brought a lamp. He passed a large pannikin under the net to me.

"What's this?" I asked.

"Benger's Food," he said. "I hope you like it."

"Did you make it?"

"Yes, on the primus; I think it's all right."

He waited while I ate the pap and then took away the empty pannikin. He tucked in the net again.

"You'll be all right now," he said.

He limped out, closing the door quietly behind him.

My mind was clear when I woke in the morning. Woodley was standing near my bed lathering his chin. He turned round when I moved.

"How are you?" he enquired cheerfully.

"Better," I said, pushing away the net.

He stopped lathering and with brush poised regarded me earnestly.

"You look much better, but you'll have to be careful," he said.

He brought me breakfast, but he allowed me to get up afterwards and sit in a deck-chair. A canoe from the mainland came for him and I was left to myself.

There had been a strong west wind on the beam when we left Pepesala in the Russell Islands; it had blown harder when we got away from the land and the *Wai-ai* had heeled over with the rail under water. I had stood astern holding on to the cabin house until all at once I had felt overwhelming fatigue. That had been three days before, and I had remembered nothing after that until I woke in Woodley's house. I was interrupted in my reflections by Hiro coming up the verandah steps. He told me I had been delirious and that he and Atiu had held me in my bunk during the crossing. They had brought me to Burutu and Woodley had sat up two nights with me. I thought I must have had cerebral malaria.

I stayed three more days at the mission house and then Woodley, unwilling for me to go, helped me along the narrow path to the jetty. He was embarrassed when I thanked him. "I'm glad I was here," was all he said.

I wrote to Woodley when I got back and told him he would always be welcome at Tataba. Our association became closer than it had been before our quarrel. We lent each other books and talked together for hours when we met. I copied the Bugotu grammar he had compiled and a vocabulary of more than a thousand words. He taught me the language and I helped him with photography, at which he was a beginner.

One morning during this period Joe brought oysters to the house.

"How are you, Joe. Mary belong you stop?" I spoke to him in pidgin, as we could neither of us understand each other in the vernacular.

He laughed in his slightly crazy manner, but made no reply. The old man's appearance diverted me and I was sure that his troubles had been somehow resolved. I had been away too much to keep abreast of his affairs.

"Mary belong you stop, Joe?" I asked him again.

He shook with a gust of laughter, as though my question was excruciatingly funny.

"Him he stop," he shouted.

"Altogether for Regi talk along 'um?"

"Altogether talk along 'um this time."

"Him he go for church house?"

"Him he go, him he go," he repeated delightedly.

I gave him two sticks of tobacco and he went away still laughing.

I made no enquiries how Joe's affairs had come right. I supposed Woodley must have intervened, but I thought it wise not to ask. Though neither by word nor deed did he show disapproval of any of his followers and indeed was quick to defend them against implied criticism, I had discovered that he was doing his best to moderate the harsh judgment of the more intolerant of them. He had a difficult task. There were subjects which I still found it best to avoid. Woodley had come much under the influence of the chaplain of his north-country public school who had encouraged him to be a missionary; from the time he went to Oxford he had no doubt what his life work was to be. After a few years as a curate he judged the time had come for him to enter the mission field and then the War came. But five years later he met opposition to his proposals. There were difficulties and he had been summoned by his Bishop, who had advised him to take up work for which he seemed better suited. Woodley saw a conspiracy to prevent him doing what he wanted; he believed himself a better judge of himself than those with whom he had worked. But not only was his temperament in doubt, there was uncertainty about his physical fitness for work in the tropics. Woodley was nearly forty before his persistence and the vehemence with which he pleaded overcame all difficulties placed in his way and he was accepted at last by the Pacific Islands Mission for work in the Solomons. But the complexities of his temperament and his physical shortcomings were aggravated by the hard lonely life he was compelled to live in the Islands. He seemed to me to be a man sick in mind and body. While I thought him a misguided man and knew him capable of sudden bursts of temper, there were times when I looked upon him as nearer to being a saint than anyone I had met. I marvelled at his dedication and at the degree of self-abnegation and humility he achieved. His intense singleness of purpose, his devotion to his work and his burning zeal at times bordered on fanaticism. He pursued the unattainable, he was a perfectionist in an imperfect world, and the inevitable set-backs and disappointments he suffered made him overwhelmingly despondent. On two occasions I called at Burutu and found him sitting in a deck-chair on the narrow verandah of his little house bowed down and speechless with despair and apparently lost to reason. Something had gone wrong; one of his people for whom he had hoped a lot had failed him. But I had also seen him almost beside himself with fury. At Kotubuka, a coastal village between Tataba and Maringe Lagoon, an order for a canoe to meet him had mis-carried or he had been disobeyed and he was stranded. I offered to take him up the coast in the *Wai-ai*, but he refused and instead stood on the beach castigating his people and declaring he would not move until the canoe was brought to him. No one suffered more than he did by his uncompromising demand for obedience, and it is unlikely that anyone was impressed by it. After a year I became increasingly convinced that disaster would soon overtake him. He could not drive himself as he did, canoeing up and down the coast, tramping

between villages, indifferent about food and taking no safe-
guards for his health; the breaking point somewhere would
be reached and there would be a collapse. But when disaster
did come, it did not come in the way which I had expected.
There had been a murder north of Maringe Lagoon; a man
had swung an axe at an unfaithful wife. I got back to Tataba
just after six o'clock and had typed the depositions and had sent
the accused man and witnesses to Tulagi for trial. Mosquitoes
were active in the house and my wrists were swollen and
scarred with bites. I wanted to get under the net of my bed
as soon as I could and read by a flash-light. I bathed and had
three drinks and sat in pyjamas at the table in the little dining-
room. The boy brought me boiled fish and yams. I spooned
the food on to my plate and drenched it with Worcester sauce.
The last glass chimney of the table lamp was broken and I ate
quickly by the light of a hurricane lamp. The boy took away
the empty plate and put down a fruit salad of pawpaws and
pineapples. He turned to go back to the kitchen, but paused at
a sound on the gravel outside. Messengers with letters sometimes arrived at the house after dark, but it was more likely
that I was wanted for someone who was sick. The boy crossed
the room and went through the double doorway towards the
top of the verandah steps outside. "Tell them to wait until I
have finished *kai kai*," I called after him. But as I spoke there
was a commotion. In the poor light I could not see what was
happening until Woodley, bedraggled and dirty, plunged
forward with outstretched arms towards me. I stood up and
allowed him to come to me and then pulled out a chair at the
table and helped him into it. He buried his face in his hands and
wept despairingly. His sudden arrival shocked and dismayed
me. I sent the boy out of the room, and then I stood up and
poured out some whisky from the decanter on the sideboard.
I added water from the jug on the table and touched Woodley's
back.

"Have a drink," I said.

He wept without restraint.

"Pull yourself together and have a drink," I urged him.

46

He slowly raised his head. He was red-eyed and ugly from weeping. He ignored the glass I had pushed towards him.

"It were better for me that a millstone were hanged about my neck," he mumbled and burst into renewed weeping.

"What are you talking about?" I demanded. "Where have you come from?"

I pushed the glass towards him again. "Snap out of it for goodness' sake."

He spoke as though he had not heard me.

"Who am I, a hypocrite, to have judged other men?"

"Where have you come from?"

"I've just come from Burutu."

"At this time of night?"

"Yes, I had to come."

"Tell me about it when you've had a bath," I suggested.

Woodley was very much smaller than me and the trousers I gave him after his bath bunched loosely under a belt almost up to his chest. His close set shoulders and narrow chest were lost in the shirt. He ignored the preposterously ill-fitting garments as though the misery and despair which oppressed him made them unimportant.

I took the whisky to the sitting-room and made him sit down in the chair facing me.

"Now have a drink," I told him.

He took the glass as though in a trance and slowly raised it to his mouth. Spirit splashed down the shirt front when he coughed and spluttered as he gulped the strong mixture. He put the glass on the stool beside his chair and stood up and began to pace the room.

"Sit down," I said, and topped up his glass and poured out more whisky for myself. I had not seen him for two months. He had always been thin almost to emaciation, but now, tremulous and distraught with emotion, his appearance alarmed me.

"What's all this about?" I demanded.

He jumped up abruptly and began limping about the room again.

"I have sinned," he declared in a choking voice.

My eyes followed him as he moved jerkily to and fro.

"Sit down," I said crossly.

He returned to the chair and sat covering his face with his hands.

"What do you mean, you've sinned?" I asked.

"I've been guilty of uncleanness."

"You mean you've had a woman?"

"God forgive me, yes."

"Well, for goodness' sake, I thought something serious had happened."

"You fool," he declared, "you ignorant fool. . . ."

I cut off his passionate outburst.

"Don't be so dramatic," I said loudly, "and for God's sake sit down."

The boy peered round the door and gaped at Woodley.

"*Kai kai* ready," he said and quickly withdrew.

I touched Woodley by the elbow and shepherded him back unresisting to the dining-room. I forced him to drink some of the soup the boy had heated for him, but I could not get him to eat anything.

When we returned to the sitting-room he had recovered a little from his extreme distress and was more composed. His unexpected lapse would bring consternation to mission elders. He would have to go, I supposed, and might, with the burden of guilt upon him, give up the Church. The situation was fantastic, but I felt unable to bring comfort to the tortured unhappy man who sat with his eyes upon me answering automatically when I spoke to him.

He shook his head when I offered him whisky, but I poured out another tot for myself. Mosquitoes, invisible in the half light of the room, came through the window, their whining drone becoming louder and louder until there was silence and I felt the prick of their bites.

The nine o'clock drum sounded and then the high-pitched laughter of Constable Busa echoed up from the beach. It was not a mirthful sound; it was more a trick of expression, a rejoinder of appreciation or of agreement. I had become accustomed to it and I was unprepared for the effect it had on Woodley. He cocked his head attentively and then a look of horror came over his face. He jumped up from his chair, took a step into the middle of the room and with a tragic gesture raised his right hand to his face.

"They're laughing at me," he sobbed. "Do you hear them? They're laughing at me."

I resented the emotional stress in which Woodley had embroiled me, and I spoke sharply.

"Don't be ridiculous. That's Busa; he constantly makes that stupid noise."

But I might not have spoken for all the good I did.

"They're laughing at me, I tell you. The canoemen must have told them. Soon everyone will be laughing. I'll have to go. I can't stay here any longer."

As Woodley spoke, the neighing titter of Busa's laughter reached us again. He looked round the room frantically like a man seeking escape. I got up and took his elbow and led him back to his chair.

"You're being very stupid," I said. "I've been hearing Busa laugh like that for over a year—ever since he came here. It's nothing to do with you."

He looked at me suspiciously. "You're not lying to me?"

I pushed him gently into the chair.

"Sit down, you stupid fellow, and don't be absurd."

Woodley sat in a state of glowering abstraction. I looked at him in silence for three or four minutes. I had not been curious at first, but now I thought I ought to know the facts. He roused himself when I spoke.

"Do I know the girl?" I asked.

"Alice Loma'a," he replied unhappily.

"Alice Loma'a from Vulavu?"

"Yes."

My curiosity was aroused now. I recalled the girl and her affair with Melema, the man I had sent to Tulagi.

"How did you get mixed up with her?"

He bowed his head in his hands.

"I asked to see her when I went to her village. I wanted to know what she was doing."

I stifled a nervous impulse to laugh.

"You wanted to see if she was behaving herself."

"Yes."

"What happened?"

"She started to visit Burutu."

"Yes."

"She came to the house this afternoon when I was resting and sat on my bed."

"Yes?"

The words came out slowly as though Woodley found pain in uttering them.

"Until then I had resisted the temptation."

Minutes passed. Woodley had fallen into an abyss of gloom and I could think of nothing to say. Then I leant forward and tapped his knee.

"Listen to me," I said. "It may be better for you to leave the island, but you're a fool to lose a minute's sleep about that little bitch."

He sprang from the chair. The light was behind him and he appeared gaunt and dark in the shade.

"How dare you presume to advise me?"

"Shut up and sit down. What are you here for anyway?"

He limped across the room towards the verandah.

"Where are you going?"

He made no reply and I heard his feet on the steps leading down to the garden. I ran and overtook him on the gravel path outside. He threw off my hand when I tried to detain him.

"Come back," I said.

"I refuse to stay in your house."

I got in front of him and barred his way. When he moved to one side to pass me I put out my arm and held him.

"Let me go," he screamed, flailing wildly and beating my face.

He struggled furiously to free himself, but I was much too

heavy and strong for him. We wrestled for half a minute in front of the house, then he hung limp in my arms. I easily carried him up the steps and laid him on the spare bed. I drew a blanket over him and pulled down the net. I sent for Hiro and told him to remain at the house and give an alarm if Woodley wandered off in the night.

Woodley stayed a week with me. I became anxious about him, for he had become dispirited and silent. Once he asked me if I thought he ought to marry Alice Loma'a. I laughed at him and told him not to be absurd. Without consulting him, I sent Hiro in the *Wai-ai* to the mission station to find Woodley's boy and pack up the house. I had decided to take him to Tulagi Hospital.

Woodley became docile and amenable and would do anything I said. I made him promise to tell no one in the Islands about his unhappy frolic with Alice. He demurred at first, but agreed finally when I said it would not be fair to the girl to speak about it. I would do my best to suppress talk.

I took him to Tulagi and left him at the hospital. I told Crichton, the doctor, what had happened. He said he would arrange for Woodley to stay at mission headquarters and would advise that he should go to Sydney by the next mail-boat. Woodley was sad and disconsolate when I saw him next day at the hospital, his shabby possessions on the locker beside him. I looked back from the door when I left. I knew I would never see him again. He forced his face into a smile and raised his right arm in the gesture of a salute. There must have been more that I could have said then, but I could think of nothing. I waved my hand and went out. I had work to do at Tataba and I wanted to see Alice Loma'a and stop as much talk as I could.

Ten days later I was in Tulagi again and I had not had a chance to go round to Vulavu. Darcy said he wanted to see me and talk about some letters I had written on native trading. When he had finished with me, I crossed the harbour in the *Wai-ai* to buy provisions at Burns Philp store on Makambo Island. In contrast to the glaring sunshine outside I found it dark in the weather-boarded building and I barely noticed the man who was coming out as I entered. He stopped. "It's Mr Fowler, isn't it?" he asked. My eyes became adjusted to the dim light and I recognised him, a man named Burton, a flabby grey-haired man of fifty or more, a secretary or officer of some sort in the mission. His black tie was held in place with an elaborate gold chain attachment. He carried a topee in one hand and a small leather case in the other. I had met him once in Darcy's office and two or three times elsewhere in Tulagi.

"I'm Fowler," I replied.

He glanced furtively over his shoulder at the people standing at the store-bar and then pointed with his topee to a corner on the right of the doorway. We stood near a mass of ships' gear, coils of rope, galvanised iron anchors, and wooden blocks. He gazed at me earnestly.

"You are just the person I wanted to see."

"Yes?"

"You knew our man Woodley well?"

"Yes."

Burton cleared his throat; he was at a loss how to go on.

"He's been ill."

"I'm sorry."

"Yes, but he's much better. He left by the last mail-boat for Sydney on his way to Melbourne."

"I'm glad he's better."

Burton fingered his straggly grey moustache and looked at me doubtfully.

"It's rather a delicate matter I wanted to speak about."

"Oh, yes."

I caught a whiff of sour breath as he came closer and spoke in a whisper.

"Have you heard any rumours about him?"

"About Woodley?"

"Yes."

"No, have there been any?"

"Yes. There's a story that he had sexual relations with a black woman."

I pursed my lips and shook my head.

"Nonsense, I'd have been the first to hear anything like that."

He looked at me wide eyed and anxious.

"You don't think it's true?"

"Good heavens, no."

Burton sighed. His fleshy face was no longer puckered with anxiety.

"I'm glad. If one of our people had done anything like that, it would have caused grave scandal, grave scandal." He shook his head at the thought of it. "I suppose, too, we should have had to make a report to the Finance and General Purposes Committee in Melbourne. But if it's not true, there's nothing more to be said." His voice petered out weakly. He wiped his forehead with a sweat-towel, still looking at me, and then with a sudden return of doubt to his face, he spoke again.

"If he should ask, I can tell the Field Secretary on your authority that there is no substance in the rumour?"

"Yes, of course."

He put the topee on his head, glanced back at the store, and turned to go.

"Very sticky today again, don't you think?" he said.

He moved off, splay footed, into the sunshine outside.

I went farther into the cool gloom of the store to the bar. I sipped cold lager beer and wondered what had impelled me to lie about Woodley. We were not friends. Maybe the bond between us was stronger than ordinary friendship. Maybe I was merely sorry for him. Whatever my feelings for him, I did not want him hurt any more.

When I got back, it was time to visit villages on the southeast coast of the island, though at the back of my mind I thought more about Woodley than about my work. I speculated on the effect of his lapse and sudden departure. Perhaps because it was the sin that people were most prone to, fornication held a special place in the condemnation of the mission. It was not readily forgiven, and those who fell, were, for a time at least, treated as outcasts.

We came to Vulavu and went northward of the green rock

and came in and dropped anchor off the beach. The headman came down to the water's edge to greet me. A crowd of men and boys formed round us while we talked. The headman looked at me blankly when I sandwiched a question about Alice Loma'a with my usual enquiries.

"Who?" he asked.

"Alice Loma'a," I repeated.

He turned to people standing with him and then looked back with a smile of understanding when one of them spoke.

"I remember the girl."

"She make trouble now?"

The headman looked perplexed and consulted his people again.

"Long time now she have man; she's married, she have baby, I hear."

I wondered if the affair were more complex than I feared.

"I like to talk to her."

One of the bystanders replied.

"She's not here."

"Alice Loma'a not here!"

"She go for Bala Bala."

My interest in the girl must have seemed excessive.

"Why she go there?"

"Her husband work for plantation."

"How long she go there?"

There was an argument in the little group. One man said it was more than a year, but another denied it and said it was about nine months.

"She ever come back here?"

They shook their heads. Nobody had seen her again.

An illuminating flash made everything suddenly clear. Woodley, striving beyond the limits of human endurance, going more than the second mile with the people of the island, unable to rest, had come to me in a state of collapse tortured by an absurd hallucination which now to my bitter regret I knew I should have recognised. Almost before we had stopped talking about Alice Loma'a I spoke of Woodley's departure.

54

The headman said he had worked too hard; he was a very good man and they were sorry he had been ill. He was a very good man I told myself and it was with a pang of dismay that I realised that I had sometimes forgotten what appeared obvious to the people of the island and what I knew to be true.

Woodley sent me a bread and butter letter from Melbourne. His health was better, he wrote, he had booked a passage in the *Balranald,* he would write again when he got home. But it was months before I heard again from him. I saw his letter on the verandah floor—one of about ten I had shaken out the mail bag on a hot January afternoon in 1929. It bore a Canadian stamp but the neat scholarly handwriting was unmistakable. Woodley wrote from Horeb, a town in Saskatchewan. He liked the people there and he liked the life on the prairie. There was a snapshot of a clapboard church. He had been inducted a month before, nearly four months before his letter reached me. Woodley said he would never return to the Islands. This, I reflected, was strange. There had been much persuasion to get him to come back; even I had been approached to use what influence I had with him. He had been promised a motor launch to help him in his work along the coast and a new house. The mission seemed to find him indispensable. He was unsuited for the life in the Islands he wrote, and I knew he was right. I read his letter a second time and looked at the snapshot. Then I tore them up and tossed the scraps in the waste-paper basket. I was glad he was not returning.

CHAPTER THREE

In High Esteem

I WOKE at daylight. Beni had started the fire and blue smoke curled up from the galley funnel. There were two canoes alongside and strangers sat about aft. I walked for'ard, and Wesu with deft movement hitched the ropes of the canvas screen abaft the mast and gave me privacy. As I ate breakfast, slight ripples in the tranquil waters of the anchorage glinted in the morning sun and inflated Portuguese Men o' War drifted slowly past the ship. The bright plumage of parrots brought colour to the greenery of the rising land ashore. It was calm after the strong winds of the past two days and though it was too early to be hot, haze over the water gave promise of later heat.

We were at anchor off Laluala close in under a high woody promontory ten miles south-east of Burutu. The headman came out in a canoe to me. He was short of liniment, he said—elderly people along the coast suffered much from rheumatism —he also asked for what he called 'sore leg medicine'. I brought up from below what I could spare from my stock and looked out to sea when I had handed it overboard to him. A canoe was passing outside towards Burutu. The four men in it leaned forward as they plunged their paddle blades into the water; then they straightened, drawing the shafts towards their chests, then leaned forward again, repeating the motions with mechanical precision. They paddled at a fast rate, not with the flicks of a short spurt but like men on a journey making haste for a purpose. They did not see us until they were well past the headland. Then they stopped paddling, but two of them sliced the water with paddle blades to keep the canoe steady in the swell, until the man in the stern paddled briskly, scooping up water and turning the canoe towards us; and then all four began to paddle again. When they came within earshot, Hiro shouted.

"They are Bagana people," he said when he got a reply.

"We are going there now. If they want to talk to me, tell them to come aboard. We'll tow their canoe," I told him.

They brought the canoe alongside and three of them stood up and clambered on to the deck. The fourth man passed a rope through a ring in the stern sheets of the boat and fixed it in a loop over the prow of the canoe. Then he sat down and busied himself baling out water.

Hiro listened gravely to what the leader of the three men told him.

"What do they want?" I asked.

Hiro pursed his lips and looked uncertainly at the men, who were standing listening attentively.

"There's plenty of trouble at Bagana," he replied.

"All right, leave it until we get to Bagana; let the three men sit down."

We took a course along a coastline of mangrove swamp. The dull uninteresting scene was relieved by the sight of high trees in the distance; and as we drew near to Bagana I saw huts scattered on undulating land above the swamp which ran almost to the foothills of the mountains that rose beyond. We anchored in discoloured water a hundred yards from the edge of the mangroves.

Hiro, Hoile and Toga set off for the shore in the canoe with the Bagana people, and sped towards an opening in the swamp. The journey in the boat was wearisome. It grounded so often in the channel through the swamp that Wesu and Gagi walked one on each side manhandling it along through the dirty dark-coloured water. We were hemmed in by mangrove trees, their boles propped by arched twisting stilt-like roots. The channel was sunless and gloomy. I got an occasional glimpse of a brightly coloured beetle, blue, yellow and red, crawling

58

up a spindly root and of an amphibious creature flipping its way across pools in the swamp.

The headman with two of his people and the three constables were waiting for me at the canoe landing-place at the end of the channel. A well-trodden red clay path went sharply up two hundred feet or more to the village. Hiro and the others went ahead easily, but I sweated and gasped in the tepid stagnant air.

We reached an area of flat land where the first of the huts had been built.

"What's the trouble?" I asked Hiro.

"There's a lot of trouble over a *devil devil* man, an old man named Kabo," he replied. "Serious trouble."

"A *devil devil* man is making trouble here?"

"Yes," he said sombrely, "much trouble."

I needed time to assimilate what he told me.

"Is that what the headman says?"

"Yes, he says this *devil devil* man made two people die and now there is another man sick and about to die."

"How does he know this man Kabo caused the death of these people?"

Hiro could not conceal his impatience.

"Everybody knows it," he said shortly, and looked away.

The three constables and the headman and his attendants now waited expectantly for me to speak. I tried not to show the blank uneasiness and perplexity that I felt.

"Maybe everyone knows this," I told Hiro, "but I don't. Tell the headman to bring me two or three old men. I'll talk to them and afterwards decide what I'll do."

I opened my camp chair and sat in the shade of a breadfruit tree. They brought three old men there. They all looked over seventy, and one of them might have been eighty. Somebody turned over wooden food-pots for them to sit on. The oldest of the three took out a trade pipe with a metal cap hinged to the bowl; he smoked the local leaf and the harsh fumes made my throat sore. I talked for nearly two hours about what they called *bei*. Then I enquired about the men who had died. I asked to see the sick man and I talked to him. He was certain

59

he was bewitched and had brought someone's hate upon himself.

Hiro set up my folding table. I opened the office box, took out the court record book, placed it on the table and opened it at a new page.

Witnesses would decide what I did after that, I thought.

"Bring Kabo," I said to Hiro.

Hiro spoke to the headman and then turned to me.

"The headman says this man Kabo won't come; it is better that you see him yourself. He might obey a white man."

"All right," I said. "Toga stay here and you and Hoile come with me to see the old man."

I followed the headman through the village to Kabo's hut. The skin of his bare chest and arms was scaly with disease, and his right eye was covered with the yellow film of cataract. He was very dirty. When Hiro told him he was wanted in court, he glared at us with his good eye and raised his voice in shrill abuse. Hiro and Hoile looked abashed. "Get hold of him," I said. They each took one of the man's arms and pulled him from the log where he was sitting. After this he made no resistance, but walked back with us through the village, declaiming and shouting in a quavering voice.

I held court under the breadfruit tree. Kabo became abusive again when Hiro explained the charge, and refused to be quiet. I called one of the old men I had seen earlier.

"You know this *devil devil* thing called *bei*?"

"I know about it."

"How is it done; what happens?"

"The *devil devil* man goes *koporo* about the place at night time. He may go inside somebody's house or just search all about outside. He picks up a small piece of food such as taro, yam or a bit of areca nut, or maybe some shit or a small piece of cloth or anything belonging to the man who is to die."

"What do you mean by *koporo*?"

There was an exchange of talk between Hiro and the old man before I got a reply.

"*Koporo* is like spying."

"All right. What do you call this man who goes *koporo* at night time?"

"We call him *mane-bei*."

"*Mane-bei*?"

The old man yawned noisily, spat and rubbed his face with his hand. He looked at the people in the court under the tree.

"*Mane-bei*," he repeated.

"What happens after the *mane-bei* has taken an object such as you speak about?" I said.

"He puts it for his *padagi tidatho*, the shrine of his guardian spirit."

I said nothing, and the old man went on.

"That's a skull of an ancestor which he hides in a hole in the rocks, or inside a tree or some place inside his house where the thing can't be seen."

"Yes?" I said.

"Then the *mane-bei* talks and prays to his *padagi tidatho* and so he gets power to make a man ill until he dies."

Kabo suddenly raised his voice and cursed the old man in a paroxysm of fury. In a moment they were shrilly and incoherently shouting, both beside themselves with anger. It was some minutes before the police could quieten them. I told Kabo he would be allowed to speak later and I continued my questions.

"Why does the *mane-bei* make people die?"

"Because people pay him porpoise teeth or shell money."

"Before Government came to this place, if a man was known to be *mane-bei*, what would happen?"

"He would be killed."

The old man spoke decisively and looked at Kabo. Hiro nodded agreement. I asked Kabo if he had any questions. For a moment he did nothing, as though ignoring my enquiry; then he turned his back on me.

The sick man came to court. He said that when the moon was last new he got up at first cock-crow and went outside his hut to urinate. He saw Kabo and asked him what had brought him such a long way from his hut, but got no reply.

Next day he told the headman. Two other witnesses said they had seen Kabo moving about the village in the darkness. Kabo asked no questions.

I adjourned the court and told Toga to stay with Kabo. I took Hiro and Hoile to Kabo's house. We walked the length of the sprawling village and then up a short path to Kabo's house which was on the edge of the bush. If the skull was in the hut, I should be satisfied. I struck a match. It was dark in the hut and there was a revolting stench. I felt a chill of horror. The skull stood on a flat stone raised on a platform of lashed sticks in the corner of the hut. It had been daubed and grotesquely deformed with the hardened paste of the *titi* nut and there were markings on it in charcoal and lime. It was a monstrously repellent object. A fragment of taro, the rind of an areca nut, some human excreta and a wisp of dirty cloth lay on the stone.

"You see it?" I asked Hiro.

"I see it," he replied uneasily.

"Where's Hoile?"

"He no like it, he go outside."

We went back through the village to the table and chair under the tree and I resumed the trial. Someone exclaimed "Koi!" and there were murmurs when Hiro spoke of what he had seen. I asked Kabo if he had any witnesses or wished to speak for himself. He looked at me insolently and began to talk quickly in a loud shrill voice. I sentenced him to six months imprisonment and ordered the *padagi tidatho* to be destroyed.

I told the headman to call his people together. Then I picked up a wooden food-pestle and with a growing crowd behind me I walked through the village again, back to Kabo's hut. "Bring the thing out," I said to Hiro. He moved unwillingly towards the entrance of the hut. I pushed him aside. "Get out of the way," I said. I brought out the skull and the stone and put them down on the ground. Feeling tension in the silence of the crowd, I squatted the better to do what I intended. I smashed the skull with the food-pestle. The fragments clinked on the stone, like cups in saucers. There was a shriek, an unclean sound like that of a diseased animal. Toga, walking slowly with Kabo, had reached us and had come to the front of the crowd. Hoile helped him restrain Kabo as I picked up the flat stone and the fragments of skull and carried them forward to the point where the land dropped suddenly down to the swamp. I hurled the stone and the pieces of skull as far as I could into the depths of the dense vegetation below. A sound came from the crowd—not cheers or shouts of approval, but a concerted drawn out exclamation of wonder or relief. It increased in volume like the onset of high wind and then subsided again. There was silence as people made way for me and I walked off towards the path down to the channel. Then I hurried down the hill to the landing place. They took me back to the ship in a canoe. The tide had risen since the morning; we went through the swamp unhindered and then quickly across the water outside to the *Wai-ai*. It was quarter to five by the cabin clock. It seemed a long time since I had eaten breakfast at Japuana.

We left next day before sunrise. The wind from the southeast had freshened. At Cape Prieto we stripped off the awning and hoisted the mainsail and let the boom swing out on the mainsheet. The *Wai-ai* responded eagerly like a live thing to the following wind. At four o'clock we were off Martin Point. I felt a surge of emotion when I saw the huts of the Government Station and my house, small and remote, on the high land behind. It satisfied the most imaginative conception of an Empire Outpost; it was my station; I was in charge; it was homecoming. A native constable would be on his way up to the house to break the Union Jack as I stepped ashore.

A crowd of people had collected to meet us at the wharf. Atiu was at the top of the verandah steps when I reached the house. He had limed his head to kill lice and it had made his hair a tawny colour. I asked him what he had done while I was away. He showed me the floors he had coloured with mangrove stain and polished with coconut husk. He had splashed the white painted walls in places, but I said nothing.

The house was bare and sparsely furnished, but as I walked from room to room I was conscious of a feeling of content. The hammock on the verandah where I sometimes slept was in its right place. I caught the scent of orchids in the wire baskets hanging overhead. The view of the harbour and of the reef and sea beyond satisfied some obscure desire.

Beni came into the house with a lamp from the *Wai-ai*; he looked at Atiu but neither spoke. Prisoners' had arrived at the back of the house with baggage. "Show them where to put everything," I said to Atiu.

"There's mail," he said as he moved away.

"Where?" I asked. The mail bag was too light to contain much. I broke the seal; there were six letters tied in a bundle with tape. Except for two they were without interest. There was a letter from Longman of the Constabulary. Dolimae had been promoted sergeant and transferred to Tulagi and Corporal Tarova was to relieve him. The other letter surprised me more. I was posted to a new station at Maka in Malaita District. I was to report monthly to Mr Brayne, District Officer, Malaita, for my orders. I had developed no special liking for the island of Ysabel, but I had no wish to leave it. I read the letter again with greater care. Mr R. F. Shelton was posted to relieve me.

Shelton was a retired naval officer; he was twelve years older than I, but had been only a year longer in the Colonial Service. He was a tall, well-groomed, dark man with much charm and an engaging manner. He was becoming a little fleshy, I thought, though someone said he had once been squash rackets champion of the Navy and for two sets he was still the best tennis singles player in the Solomons. But Shelton had more than social grace and skill at games; he was a competent, self-assured man of great ability. His stock with Darcy was high; he was destined for better things, and no one supposed he would stay long in the Solomons.

He had visited Tulagi occasionally while I was there and I had met him four times—twice at the Residency and twice at the Club. The first time we set eyes on each other I was conscious of an instantaneous antipathy between us. It blazed up like a flame without reason. I knew nothing of him then and he knew nothing of me, but I disliked him and I knew he disliked me. This was curious, because Shelton was a popular man and made himself agreeable even to people whose opinion meant nothing to him. But with me he was different; he had spoken pointedly in my presence of youth and immaturity and had laughed contemptuously at the hesitant contributions I had made to discussions. Perhaps he regarded me as gauche and callow and lacked the patience to bear with me, but I think it more likely that he resented being so little senior to me in the service despite the fact that he was so much older and had had much greater experience. He was the last person to whom I would have chosen to hand over the district, but I suppressed my personal feelings. With only slight encouragement from him I would be friendly during the short time we would be together, and whatever happened I would hand over as well as I could.

Hiro swept out the office, cleaned the windows, polished the brass door-knobs and arranged the medicines on the shelves. When he had done all this he went outside and weeded the grass round the office. I pinned the fresh blotting-paper on the table and cleaned the typewriter. I inspected the police kit and checked the prison warrants. Then I wrote two pages of notes. There was not much I could do in the office, and there was even less to do at the house.

I sighted the *Hygeia* at four o'clock in the afternoon on the day she was due. I had tea and walked down to the wharf to meet her. It was just after five o'clock when she tied up. Bandy Coot waved his hand and shouted something I did not hear. I looked under the awning for Shelton; he was sitting in a deck-chair with a tea tray on a small table at his side. He was reading and did not look up until I greeted him. He spoke testily, as though he resented the interruption.

"Oh, good-afternoon," he said.

"Come up to the house for dinner and a bed tonight," I suggested.

He seemed startled by my invitation and shook his head immediately.

"Oh no, thank you," he replied decisively. "I'll see you at the office in the morning."

"I've got a bed made up for you," I said rather lamely.

He frowned at me in silence. "Send prisoners down for my gear in the morning," he said, replacing his spectacles and looking down again at his book.

I was nonplussed by his manner and could think of nothing to say. I walked the length of the wharf and went slowly up the hill to the house.

Shelton arrived at the office at nine o'clock in the morning; he was out of breath from the climb up the hill. He was a strongly built man, but his features seemed fine drawn and his complexion was sallow. He looked older than I knew him to be.

"I'll see the cash book first," he said.

He checked the accounts with great care.

"Three hundred and twenty pounds seventeen shillings and fourpence?" he asked when he had finished.

"That's what I make it," I said.

"Well, let me see it," he demanded.

I took out the key and went to open the safe; the keyhole was filled with red mud. "Look at this," I said. "A wasp nest since yesterday afternoon."

"If you don't keep the flap down, that's bound to happen," he said. "Even you have been out here long enough to know that."

I cleaned out the keyhole and opened the safe. The cash was in five pounds *rouleaux* of shillings; there were sixty four of them and seventeen shillings and fourpence over. I carried the money to the table and set it out for Shelton to count. He tested the weight of each of the *rouleaux* and set aside ten which he opened and counted. "Right," he said suddenly, "put it back." I felt a stab of resentment at this curt command. "I suggest you take your share," I said. He got up without a word and helped me carry the money back to the safe. I gave him the key.

Shelton examined the contents of cupboards with apparent distaste. He took out the two bulky files of letters. "Slightly less primitive methods of filing might have been devised," he said. He opened the file of out-going letters. My last letter had been about the *Wai-ai*, and instead of a reference number I had typed "*Wai-ai*" in the top left-hand corner. This mild eccentricity seemed more than he could bear; he stuttered with exasperation. He was scornful about my notes and disputed my opinions. I avoided argument and suggested he might like to see the barrack and the prison. We saw the prison first and then went down the hill to the barrack. I set a brisk pace back to the office, increasing it as we climbed up the hill. Shelton was distressed when we got to the top. He said he had seen all he wanted to see and asked me to give him lunch. "What's this muck on the floor?" he asked when we got to the house. "Mangrove stain," I replied. "It's quite a well-known way of treating floors. Would you like a gin or beer?" He declined my offer and took a bottle of Hennessy's brandy from one of his boxes. He poured himself half a glass and gulped it neat. Then he asked for water and shook out four tablets of quinine from a bottle and swallowed them with a draft.

We had a yam shepherd's pie for lunch. Shelton poked at a small helping and ate a little of it. "This tastes like blotting-paper," he said. He ate none of the fruit salad which followed. When we got up, he went straight to the room he had made his bedroom. I rested for half an hour and then went down to the *Hygeia*. Coot suggested that I should have supper and sleep aboard, so that he could leave at first light in the morning. There was nothing to take me back to the house.

At tea one of the crew handed Coot a scrap of paper.

"What's this?" he asked.

"Boy belong Mis' Shelton bring 'um," he said.

Coot peered at the paper; it was a leaf torn from a diary.

"Shelton thinks he's ill," he said slowly. "He wants us to go up there."

"We'd better see what's wrong," I said.

Coot was unperturbed. "Let's finish tea first," he said.

"Does he say what's the matter with him?"

Coot handed me the note. The scrawl told me no more than Coot had said.

Coot bathed and changed after tea. It was nearly six o'clock when we started slowly up the hill.

"You're lucky," Coot said suddenly.

"Why am I lucky?" I asked.

"Maka's the best station in the Solomons."

"Tataba's good enough for me."

"Wait till you see Maka; no one's been there before; it's all new."

"Maybe, but I don't think I'll like being on the Maramasike Passage at North Malaita."

"What!—there's a lovely view and plenty of fish. Anything will grow there."

"Yes, and Malaita men to deal with all day long."

"They're all right; they won't give you any trouble."

"It sounds all right, but I like this place and I don't want to leave it."

We had reached the house and we went into the bedroom. Shelton was lying on the bed naked, but he had drawn a sheet over himself. He complained of headache and of pains in his loins and in the region of his liver. His skin and the whites of his eyes had taken on a saffron tint. On the bedside table there was a half-pint glass of what appeared to be port.

"What's that?" I asked.

"Pee," he replied.

I was disturbed, but Coot belittled Shelton's complaints. "You'll be all right in a couple of days; you hit it up too much in Tulagi."

I said nothing. I knew Shelton was desperately ill, far worse than I had expected.

Shelton's boy brought a thermometer from the bathroom. Shelton's temperature was 104.2 degrees.

"What is it?" he murmured.

68

"It's pretty high."

"It feels about 102."

I drew Coot towards the verandah.

"He's got blackwater," I said. "He's very sick."

"What d'you want to do?"

"We've got to take him back to Tulagi."

"Anything you say, brother."

"Can we leave now?"

"Better about eight o'clock; there's a good moon and the wind'll drop. We'll be in Tulagi by five or six in the morning."

"We'll do that."

Coot went back to the *Hygeia* to warn his crew. I sent one of Shelton's boys for Hiro and told the other to make jugs of squash from lemons in the garden. I sprayed the room with insecticide to drive away flies, but they soon returned. When Hiro came, I sent him back to tell Dolimae I wanted six constables at the house at about quarter to eight.

My medical handbook gave the treatment for blackwater fever as rest and keeping the kidneys active by frequent drinks. I plied Shelton with lemon squash and encouraged him to urinate. The urine had become much darker and very thick.

Coot came back to the house at half-past seven.

"We're all set and ready to go," he said.

The police came soon after. They lashed poles together and made a litter eight feet by four. We wrapped Shelton in blankets and the police got their hands under the mattress and lifted it out gently to the litter on the verandah floor. When they had gone down the steps they raised the litter to the full stretch of their arms and carried it this way down the path. Flying foxes squeaked in the banyan tree behind the house. I could hear a screech owl somewhere away in the bush; cicadas kept up their incessant chirruping. Coot and I walked in silence behind the police. The wind had dropped as he had predicted, but I saw ragged clouds scudding past the moon. The roar of the surf on the reef rose and fell, louder, it seemed, than by day, and the white line of breakers caught something of the moonlight and could be plainly seen.

The police laid the mattress on the engine-room housing immediately abaft the chart-house bulkhead. Coot had tied down the canvas side-screens of the awning to make a shelter. Though there was little wind, we ran into a head sea as soon as we left the harbour and the *Hygeia* began to pitch slightly. Shelton lay still. I held a glass of lemon squash to his mouth for him to drink and made him urinate as often as he could into a jam jar. In the dim light of the hurricane lamp I could see no sign of his urine clearing: in fact, I began to fear it was becoming darker and more viscous.

Two hours after we passed Cape Prieto, Coot came aft. I looked out and saw we were passing Rua Dika.

"We are making good time," I said.

"Yes, we are doing all right," he replied. "Want me to reduce speed to keep her steadier?"

"No, we're all right; the sooner we get to Tulagi the better."

"O.K. brother, anything you say; let me know if you want me to go slower."

He went back to the chart house and I sat watching Shelton. He had not spoken for a long time. I had stopped pressing fluid on him and allowed him to sleep. At half-past two he enquired where we were. I looked out and recognised the island of Buena Vista. We were across the open sea and would be in Tulagi in two or three hours, I told him.

"You oughtn't to do this," he whispered wearily.

"Why not?" I asked.

"I don't know; you are a good nurse."

He said nothing more. He either fell asleep or passed into a coma. It was early dawn when we reached Tulagi. Riding lights of craft in the harbour and leading lights ashore were still burning. It was just half-past five when we tied up at Government Wharf. One of the crew lifted down the navigation lights and put them out. I ran to the hospital and with the flat of my hand banged on the verandah door of the nursing sister's quarters. There was immediate response. "Yes, I'm coming." I recognised the voice of the sister. She came to the verandah door, buttoning her uniform overall. "Let me send a stretcher," she said before I had finished talking. "Tell me the rest afterwards."

A launch with a noisy engine crossed the harbour; smoke began to curl up from houses on the hill; a few boys appeared lounging about the boat-house and wharf. It was daylight, and Tulagi was waking up. I shaved and put on fresh clothes and at eight o'clock I went up to Darcy's office. He listened attentively as, mumbling with fatigue, I told him what had happened. Without a word to me he picked up the telephone and spoke to his wife. Then he turned to me and told me to go to the Residency. I slept until one o'clock; Darcy had returned from the office for lunch. Crichton, the doctor, had told him Shelton was not expected to recover.

In the afternoon, on the way to the Club, I overtook Lang, the works foreman. "It's nice to see you in Tulagi again," he said, "even though it was a melancholy task which brought you." The wind had got up and a heavy sea was running. "It looks as though you got here just in time," he added.

Lang and I watched four Australians playing tennis. When they came off, disputing among themselves with a lot of jocular abuse, we went up the steps into the Club. Lang was talking about the *Wai-ai* and I wished he could have continued, but a party of men were drinking at the long table outside the bar and Perry the engineer off the *Mahaga* hailed me.

"I hear you saved Shelton's life," he said. "Have a drink."

I sat down. "It's not certain he'll live," I replied.

Houston, a bore with a great store of fragmentary information, a tiresome person, moved towards the table.

"Never move a blackwater case," he said. "If there is no house near by, a native hut or tent should be erected over the patient and he should be treated there. If travelling is unavoidable, he should be given an anaesthetic to reduce the risk of syncope."

"Well, for God's sake, Mick," Perry said in mock amazement. "What does syncope mean?"

"Collapse, heart failure," said Houston promptly.

A red-faced man sitting across the table put down his glass.

71

"Talk sense, Mick," he said. "You reckon the doctor and sister should have left the patients in Tulagi and gone out to Ysabel on Mr Fowler's word? In any case, look at the sea now."

Houston was confused. "I am not saying Mr Fowler did wrong," he started to say.

"Shut up," someone said.

I was given a drink and Perry asked me about Ysabel.

Darcy was cheerful at tea-time on the third day. Crichton had telephoned that Shelton was better; the worst was over he thought. That morning he had been in despair; he had said Shelton would not last the day. At eleven o'clock Shelton had been lucid and had asked for a gin-sling. The Sister went to her quarters and mixed it; then she held him up and helped him to drink it. When Crichton saw him at five o'clock he said he was no longer dangerously ill.

Darcy said the wind had dropped when he came in from golf that evening. It had veered round to the east-south-east and a period of settled weather was expected. He said it was time I went back to my station. When I enquired after dinner, he told me that I should now remain at Tataba until the end of my tour.

Tarova, the new corporal, was waiting at the wharf when I went down to the *Hygeia* next morning. He was a tall bushy haired native of Guadalcanal. He lacked the smartness and correct manner of Dolimae.

We reached Tataba at three o'clock. A small crowd had assembled on the wharf to meet us. When we had made fast and I had stepped ashore, Dolimae came forward and saluted.

"Everything all right for station," he reported, "but trouble at Regi."

"What's this trouble?" I asked.

"It's not big trouble, but plenty of talk," he said.

I looked at him waiting to hear more, then I saw Palukue walking hurriedly along the wharf towards us. Dolimae turned towards him for a moment, muttered, and went after Tarova.

72

The house at Tataba

The harbour, Tataba

Hiro and Wetera

"There is much trouble at Regi," Palukue said breathlessly. "I want to bring the people to you."

"I can't see them today," I told him firmly. "I shall be busy until night time. Bring them in the morning."

"I would like you to see them now," he pleaded anxiously.

"Tomorrow morning." I repeated.

I ignored Palukue. He seemed reluctant to go, hopeful perhaps that I would relent and see his people.

Coot stopped the *Hygeia's* engine barely long enough for crew and prisoners to off-load my baggage at the wharf. Before I reached the office I could hear the purr of the diesel engines, and when I looked back the vessel was already round the marking buoys and making for the passage through the reef. Almost at once reaction set in and my spirits drooped. I no longer thought of the events of the past few days; my mind turned to the day Shelton had spent with me in the station. Mounting fever and weariness had given a sharp edge to his censure, but his criticism and fault-finding were probably justified, I thought. The well-being I had felt after my action at Bagana and the return to the station and the growing confidence which had begun to come to me were all dispelled. My self-esteem had suffered grievously. I saw myself as he must have seen me, callow, muddling, inexperienced, apt to act irrationally and ill-equipped for the burden of responsibility that had been thrust on me.

I still felt a lack of confidence in myself next morning as I walked down to the office after breakfast. I gazed with misgiving at the men, women and children crowded together waiting for me. There were two groups—one congregated under the mango tree and the other standing ten yards away in the sun. Palukue came to meet me on the path. There was urgency in his manner; he did not wait for a reply to his hasty greeting.

"Two of my elders have quarrelled and my people are divided among themselves; there is much trouble at Regi." Palukue's speech had a slightly biblical flavour. He fell in with me walking at my side.

73

"Give me a chance," I said crossly. "Let me get to the office and sit down."

Hiro saluted me at the door. People from the mango tree and from the other group began to surge forward.

"Tell them to keep away until I am ready," I said.

I went into the office and sat down at the table.

"Let Palukue come now," I told Hiro.

Palukue had a worried expression; he looked harassed. I began to wonder whether he was concerned less with the welfare of his people than with finding relief from the cares of office.

"What's the matter?" I asked.

He sighed. "The wife of Raji has confessed that she has had sexual intercourse with Wolomi and now Raji has cursed Wolomi and Wolomi is angry."

"Can't you settle this?"

"No, it is too much for me. If I say one thing, half the people will hate me."

"Let the two men and their women come in," I said to Hiro. "I want to see no one else."

Raji was the canoe-maker I had watched at work, a big round-faced, muscular man with a moustache and thin fuzzy hair. He looked in a bad temper. His wife stood behind, pigeon-toed and with her eyes on the ground. She had an infant on her hip. She seemed very frightened. The other man, Wolomi, had a light skin and close-set features, a difficult, intolerant-looking man who could be spiteful and vicious, I thought. His wife had limed close-cropped hair. Her stomach bulged out over the band of her cloth as though she were pregnant.

I found it a preposterous situation. I looked at the baby on the hip of Raji's wife and then at Palukue.

"Is Wolomi the father of this child?" I asked.

Palukue was shocked. "Oh dear me, no," he said gazing in turn at everyone in the room.

"You told me the woman admitted that Wolomi had been with her."

"Yes, she confessed that she had sinned with Wolomi."

74

In High Esteem

"When?"

Palukue spoke to the woman. Raji scowled and seemed about to speak, but changed his mind. His wife replied in a whisper without looking up.

"About ten years ago," Palukue said.

"Ten years ago!" I exclaimed. "Why bring it up now and cause all this trouble?"

"It is because she feared death."

"What do you mean?" I asked in surprise. "Why should she fear death?"

"This woman went to the bush to have this child, but the child was big and she strove for two days in great pain; she thought she would die. Our people believe that woman's trouble in child bearing is because she is defiled by past sin. This woman was told to purge herself by naming the men who have lain with her. It is a heathen custom."

"Was the baby born all right."

"Oh yes, the baby is all right."

"When this woman was in great distress she talked about the men who had been with her and the women who heard then told everyone?"

"Yes."

"How many men did she name?"

The baby whimpered and then started to wail with imperious insistence. My question was lost in the noise. Hiro exclaimed at the woman in a sharp staccato tone. She lifted the baby round to her bosom and gave it a breast and there was silence.

"How many men did she name?" I asked again.

"Two."

"Only two?"

"Yes, her husband and Wolomi."

"How long has she been married?"

Palukue turned to Raji.

"Raji says they were married about seven years ago," he said.

"Wolomi went with the woman before she was married then?"

75

"I don't know."

"Count the years or, if you like, ask the woman herself."

I moved my face away cautiously; a hornet flew buzzing near me. It was building a red mud nest for its egg against a rafter in the thatch above my head. Everyone in the room looked at me with concern as I moved my head evasively. Then the hornet flew up with its tiny dollop of mud and Palukue spoke to the woman. Wolomi interrupted in a loud and aggressive voice and the woman had no chance to reply. The next moment Raji was shouting furiously at Wolomi. There was uproar until Hiro went to each man in turn and spoke severely.

"What's all that about?" I asked him.

"Wolomi says this woman was not married when he had her. Raji says he had paid the woman's father three hundred red shell money and had taken the woman and put her with his mother. He says everyone in Regi knew this. Then Raji and Wolomi get angry with each other and want to fight."

"Yes, all right," I said; and then I turned to Palukue again. "You say Raji cursed Wolomi when he was told what his wife had said?"

"Yes, he cursed him and made Wolomi very cross."

"What was this curse?"

Palukue replied as though searching for words. "Excreta on your head," he said hesitantly.

"He said 'Shit on your head' like the Malaita curse. Is that a bad curse?"

"Not very bad, but people don't like it."

"What would happen if Government wasn't here?"

"There might be a fight and one man get killed."

"Take your people out," I said to Palukue. "I'll speak to everyone outside."

I walked out on to the grassy expanse. I did not know what I was going to say, but I found myself talking. I told them I was surprised that such an advanced community as the Regi people should waste time on petty quarrels. I said it was not what I expected of them. I said they ought to be ashamed of themselves. I could not go on repeating myself, I had to finish somehow. I ordered Wolomi to pay Raji one hundred porpoise teeth for seducing an affianced woman; then I faced Raji and his followers under the mango tree and ordered him to pay Wolomi one hundred porpoise teeth as compensation for swearing at him. There was no outcry; no one spoke. I went back to the office and lit a cigarette. The crowd moved off silently down the path to the beach on the way back to Regi. I looked at my watch; it was ten o'clock. The Regi people had been with me for two hours.

I went down to the barrack and walked slowly round the station. There was little to do in the office, and I read law for an hour. At half-past twelve Hiro came in and hovered silently in front of the table.

"What's the matter?" I asked.

"Palukue's here," he replied.

I was displeased. There was nothing more I could do for the Regi people. I looked down again at my book.

Hiro went out, but returned almost immediately.

"He hasn't got much to say."

A conscientious scruple triumphed over my desire to turn my back on Palukue and his problems.

"All right, let him come in; but I can't hear a lot of talk. It's close up to time for *kai kai*."

Palukue looked happy and was smiling when he entered the office.

"I'm sorry to take up your time, sir, but I have come only to say that strife at Regi has ended."

"Have Raji and Wolomi paid the one hundred porpoise teeth?"

"Yes, they have done that and peace now reigns."

"I am glad to hear that; thank you for coming to tell me."

I stood up to dismiss him, but he made no move to go.

"There's just one more thing, sir."

"Yes?"

"The Regi people say that you are a man of very great wisdom and that you love them. They are all very glad that

77

you are staying here and they pray that you will remain here for ever."

The words may have meant little, but their effect on me was immediate. I walked round the table to Palukue and escorted him to the door and then outside to the grass.

"Tell them that's very kind of them," I said, "and tell them I'm glad to be staying here too."

Palukue, still smiling happily, went off fussily down the path to the beach. He had done a lot of walking during the morning.

CHAPTER FOUR

Jardine

NORTHWARD of Burutu, twenty miles across Thousand Ships Bay, is the Ortega Channel which separates St George's Island from the mainland and links the head of the bay with the sea beyond. Sticks marked a passage through the discoloured water of the passage, but Wesu, standing for'ard with the lead-line, called soundings and we went ahead cautiously at slow speed. We anchored off Kaevaga, where the channel was narrowest.

I walked about ashore and inspected the village with Hiro and the headman and two of his attendants. On St George's Island, across the channel, two flat-topped mountains, with a deep gap between them, stood out rocky and bare in contrast to the luxuriant verdure on the slopes of the mainland. The four men waited while I gazed in silence across the water.

"Anyone live there?" I asked.

Hiro promptly replied, "No," and one of the headman's attendants who had talked freely, pushed himself forward slightly. "The island is very *tabu* for our people," he said.

"Why is it *tabu*?"

"It is the place of *tarunga,* the abode of the dead."

"You mean it is haunted by spirits or *devil devils*?"

"*Tarunga* is a dead man who after burial rises up and goes to Tuhilagi."

"You call this island Tuhilagi?"

"Yes, the place of the dead."

The man needed no encouragement to talk.

"There are many *tarunga* on Tuhilagi," he added. "Their

79

leader is Bolofaginia." He lifted his chin and turned towards the island.

"Is Bolofaginia like God?" I asked.

He shook his head, and Hiro said something.

"Bolofaginia is the first of the *tarunga,* the chief of Tuhilagi," the man said. He took out a piece of areca nut and some betel leaf from his fibre shoulder-bag and put the nut and leaf in his mouth. His companion handed him a small gourd, and with a short spatula he picked out a nugget of lime and added it to the nut and leaf in his mouth.

"What's your name?" I asked him, but it was the headman who replied. "Rage," he said.

"All right, Rage," I said. "Has anyone seen these *tarunga* you speak of?"

He shook his head decisively. "No man has seen them, but some people have seen their foot-marks and have heard their voices."

"Have you?"

"No, I've not heard them, but once I went ashore at Tuhilagi and saw the foot-marks of *tarunga* and fish and taro which they had left for us."

Hiro had shifted restlessly while Rage talked.

"This man is liar," he suddenly exclaimed in a scornful voice. "He has never been ashore at Tuhilagi, he would be too frightened; I know him."

Rage's companion and the headman joined in the altercation; there were raised voices, and Rage, gesticulating, turned from one to another as though for support.

I told them to be quiet. The sky had become overcast and there was a poor light but I saw what I thought was an area of planted coconuts on the flat coastal land of the island.

"Who do the coconuts on the other side belong to?" I asked the headman.

"That is Paul's place," he replied.

"Paul?"

"Yes, Paul, a white man."

I looked from the headman to his attendants.

"You said the place was very *tabu*."

"It is *tabu* for us black men, but the ways of white men are different."

"You know this white man?" I asked Hiro.

"Yes. Mr Jardine."

"Mr Jardine? What does he do over there?"

"He makes copra, but not very much."

"Did Major Barrington ever see him?"

"Yes, sometimes."

From the point where we were standing the channel was about half a mile wide. I had some food and rested, and then crossed to the island later in the afternoon. We anchored, and Wesu and Gagi took me ashore in the boat. There had been a wharf once, but the timbers had rotted away and now only a few barnacle-encrusted posts remained. Just above the sandy water edge a small tree stood in isolation; and there, on a short branch, a kingfisher perched. I told the crew to stop rowing and stared with astonishment at the bird. It was bigger than any kingfisher I had ever seen before. Its head and breast were snowy white and its back a lustrous cupreous green. I watched it for perhaps a minute, then it swooped down and flew low over the water to our right, turned, and with a flap of wings flew back to perch again somewhere farther along the shore.

The boat beached on coarse grey sand near the remains of the wharf. An air of abandonment pervaded the place. Undergrowth spread unchecked between the lines of stunted palms and would soon take complete possession. A hundred yards or more away someone was coming down a thin thread of a path. When he drew nearer I saw that it was a man of singular appearance. His face had fallen in as though he had lost his teeth, a beard straggled untrimmed and shapeless over his chest, and his uncut hair lay over his ears and down his neck. He was tall, very thin and with his piercing blue eyes he was a disconcerting figure. He wore, whether in my honour or not, I was unable to say, a very ill-fitting pair of calico trousers and a shirt of the same material which he had apparently made himself. What was worse was the little hat he wore to shield his head from the sun.

I told him my name and that I was the District Officer.

"Good-afternoon," he said. "I am delighted to see you. Come along to the house."

Though he was troubled in his speech by a lack of teeth, he spoke with a cultivated voice.

"You've relieved poor old Barrington," he mused as we walked along the path. "Poor old chap, he had been out here quite long enough."

As we walked, a hut came into sight. It was partly hidden among the coconut palms by pawpaw trees and a clump of banana plants. It looked very small, and when we drew nearer I saw that it was in poor condition.

"I must apologise for the house," Jardine said. "It will just have to last until the plantation comes into production; I shall build a bungalow then." There was a brief silence and he added cryptically, "but it may be possible before then."

The floor of the hut was raised. There were three steps up to it supported on posts driven into the ground. An island type of chair—canvas, in a heavy wooden frame with extended arms for leg rests—appeared to be the only furniture; but later I saw a small table nailed together from packing cases, and along the leaf-thatch wall some shelving had been fixed. The floor near the chair was littered with old picture papers.

"Take the chair," Jardine said, and then he went through an opening in the thatch partition and returned with a folding camp-chair.

"You would be too heavy for this," he said.

He sat down and rested his hands in his lap. They were sensitive hands with long tapering fingers and oval finger nails.

"Do you get any visitors?" I asked.

"Not many. Sam Petrie is very good; he picks up my copra and brings out stuff from Tulagi for me. Woodley, the missionary, was here once."

A fowl fluttered up the steps and picked its way about the

room, leaving droppings on the rough-hewn flooring. Mating lizards scampered through the opening to the place beyond.

"It's raining," I said.

The darkening sky had threatened rain for half the day.

"Yes, it is quite heavy," Jardine replied.

The place must have been depressing even when the sun shone, but now, with rain falling and water leaking through the thatch, there was indescribable melancholy about it. Jardine betrayed a slight annoyance when the rain dropped on him, and twice in a fit of frenzy he drove fowls out of the room, but most of the time he seemed indifferent to his surroundings.

As we sat watching the rain a middle-aged native came silently into the room from a back entrance. His only clothing was a scrap of cloth passed between his legs and cunningly fastened round his waist. His features were wizened and he was slightly hunchbacked.

"Ah, here is Joel," Jardine said good-humouredly. "He's my Man Friday."

The native said something in a low husky voice.

"Very well, Joel," Jardine said in reply. "Put the copra out of the rain and stop."

Jardine turned to me again. "Joel is very faithful," he said. "He comes over here from Kaevaga every day, brings a fish or a yam and makes himself useful about the place until evening."

The native disappeared as silently as he had come. A few minutes later he reappeared and squatted on his haunches against the flimsy partition.

I talked for a time with Jardine but he seemed pre-occupied and inattentive. Then he interrupted me. "I'd like to show you something," he said abruptly. He spoke to Joel and they went through the opening in the partition and returned awkwardly carrying a heavy wooden case. They put it near my chair and Jardine moved to the other side. He was breathless after his exertions.

"I'd like to show you something," he repeated. He handed

me pieces of rock from the box. Time after time he asked, "What do you think of that?" He spoke as though he was inviting an opinion on something about which he had no doubt.

The stones were certainly strange to me. There were many which glinted with specks of yellow metal; there were various lumps of crystal and there was something which flaked like mica.

Joel replaced the stones in the box.

"What do you think of them?" Jardine demanded.

"They are all very interesting," I said. "I've never seen anything like them before."

"They are more than interesting," he said. "There are valuable mineral deposits on this island, and not very far from this house at that. I am certain of it, absolutely certain of it."

He got up and walked about the little room muttering to himself; he had forgotten I was there.

"Have you had assay reports?" I asked after a pause.

"Sam has sent to Brisbane, but I am not at all satisfied with the reports, not at all satisfied," Jardine said, shaking his head impatiently.

He had become very agitated and was trembling violently. I changed the subject as soon as I could and asked him about the interior of the island. He spoke of caves and strange land formations and of places where he had heard subterranean rumbles. What he said explained much of the awe that the natives felt for the island.

It must have been five o'clock when I got up to go. It had stopped raining and the sky had lightened. Jardine looked at me with surprise. "You are not going yet?" he exclaimed. "You must stop and have *kai kai*."

He spoke very earnestly, almost anxiously.

"It's very kind of you," I said. I sat down again; it was the right thing to do, I thought.

Jardine looked pleased. "We'll have eggs and mushrooms on toast," he said. "Sam brought me flour and a tin of butter last time he was here."

He chattered as he moved to and fro through the partition opening. "What do you think of that?" he asked handing me a large brown-crusted loaf.

"It's excellent," I said.

"The yeast is the secret," he declared. "Rice and salt water. I cork it down in a bottle and leave it a few days. It makes perfect yeast."

He went somewhere at the back of the hut with Joel. I looked at the old illustrated papers while I waited. When he returned, Joel was following him and clumsily set down on the table a dish of slices of toast covered with fried eggs and mushrooms.

"I cultivate mushrooms on rotten ivory-nut logs. Did you know you could do that?" Jardine asked. "You need not fear. These are the genuine thing." He tittered without waiting for my reply.

We sat at the table set with Jardine's pitiful collection of crockery. We moved our chairs back after the meal and drank one cup of tea after another. I may have been hungry or there may have been something exceptional about Jardine's cooking. I had enjoyed the food more than any I could remember.

Joel got up at the first sign of sunset. Jardine courteously thanked him and bade him good-night. I left soon afterwards. Jardine made no attempt to detain me; I suspected that he had no lamp in the hut.

Jardine walked with me as far as the waterside. "It's been nice meeting you," he said politely. "Come again when you are this way." I thanked him for the delicious meal and said I would call next time I was at Kaevaga. We shook hands, but he stood for a few minutes where I left him. I looked back at him twice from the boat and he waved each time. The third time I looked I saw that he had turned and was making his way along the path through the derelict plantation back to the little hut.

From then on I always called on Jardine when I anchored in Ortega Channel. I found myself looking forward to seeing him on my tours of the south-east end of the island. When we sat talking, as we often did for hours, I marvelled at the way in which he ignored the gross discomforts of his surroundings. He never mentioned his poverty; by some miracle of self-deception he had convinced himself that he suffered from no more than temporary shortage of cash; at any moment, his manner seemed to imply, his efforts would be liberally rewarded. His stories absorbed me; I sat listening to them oblivious of the bleak surroundings and of the naked Melanesian who as often as not squatted on his heels against the partition, watching me in silence. I got to know something of Jardine's past. After the Boer War, instead of returning to Oxford and reading law as his parents had planned, he had stayed on in South Africa footloose and restless until a man in a bar in Johannesburg, a complete stranger, had told him stories of the Solomons and of a fabulous character named Stapleton. Jardine had raised enough money for a passage from Durban to Fremantle and had then worked his way across Australia to Sydney. He had gone up the coast to Brisbane and then on to Townsville and had got a passage in the labour schooner *Roderick Dhu,* taking Solomon Islanders home from the Queensland sugar estates. At Tulagi someone had put him aboard a schooner bound for the Roviana Lagoon in the Western Solomons where Stapleton lived.

Stapleton was the first white man to plant coconuts in the Solomons. In the early 'nineties, his neighbours were head-hunters, and the *tabu* houses of their villages were adorned with the grisly trophies of their raids. He obtained the protection of the chiefs by supplying them with weapons, and undeterred by their savage customs worked in their midst making money from everything he did—freighting between islands, trading, labour recruiting, boat building. When other people were beginning, he was established and his help was often wanted. He got grandiose notions of expansion and lured young men to join him—deserters from ships, hard men from Australia, Scandinavian sailors, misfits and wanderers of all kinds. Between intervals of work they sat in the large rambling house Stapleton had built at the edge of Roviana Lagoon drinking whisky and counting the gold sovereigns they had made while their chattering women and half-caste children prepared food and waited on them. Jardine was different from his companions; though friendly he was sensitive and gentle. The others could not understand him; some of them called him mister and treated him with greater respect than they showed even for Stapleton. Jardine inherited three thousand pounds from his parents. He loaded a schooner with seed-nuts and went to St George's Island. The island was infertile, uninhabited and away from normal schooner traffic; and there was a bigger objection; it was the traditional home of the dead, the after-world, and even if natives could be found to work there by day there was none who would remain after dark. Jardine said he liked the view from St George's Island of Ortega Channel and the green wooded hills of the mainland. No one could afford to be so eccentric without money; it was believed that he would soon tire of St George's Island and depart.

The price of copra fell during the late 'twenties, and Stapleton's empire crumbled and finally collapsed. His big house on the edge of Roviana Lagoon fell into disrepair and worm bored the timbers of his schooner and she lay rotting at the wharf in front of the house. His stores and sheds were cluttered with useless lumber. People whom he had helped in his earlier days put commissions in his way, but he was past his prime and the effort of adjusting himself to the new conditions was too much for him and he died. A few of his protégés had wandered off up to New Guinea or back to Australia; some had turned native and had fathered half-caste families; one or two, more careful than the others, were holding their own and waiting for better times. Jardine on St George's Island was as far removed from the world as though he had been on Mars. Petrie told me more about Jardine one day in Elkington's Hotel in Tulagi. He was among some people who came into the bar while I was waiting for dinner. I knew that he called regularly at St George's Island every six weeks, but I had never seen him there; and he was so often away from his own place at Loga

Point that I had stopped calling. He looked at me with some surprise when I enquired about Jardine, but he was willing to talk.

The little plantation was backward, and before it had started to produce the slump had set in. Petrie loaded a bag or two of copra when he called and made it appear that it gave credit enough for the provisions he brought back for Jardine.

"How is the copra produced?" I asked.

He shrugged his shoulders. "Paul and Joel do it between them; I suppose Paul splits the nuts and Joel cuts out the copra. It must be a fantastic sight."

"You are good to him."

Petrie flushed. "Paul and I were new chums together," he said. "He wasn't like the rest of us. He used to get invitations to play tennis at the Residency. Then in 1914 he went down to Sydney and joined up; when he came back in 1919 a lot of us had got a start on him. I reckon we owed him something. Paul was a fine-looking man, but he was never cut out for the life here. No practical man would try to grow coconuts on St George's Island."

Petrie regarded me sombrely, and then as an afterthought he demanded, "Have you ever heard him complain?"

"No, never."

"No one has."

Seven or eight people were now milling amiably about at the bar. We took our drinks to deck-chairs on the verandah and gazed at the riding lights of craft in the harbour.

"He got an idea his bit of copra wasn't paying for the stores I brought him and for a time he refused to take anything without an account. I grubstaked him then, and he went fossicking all over the hills on that island. There might have been something in it, I thought."

The hotel boy brought the bottle and Petrie signed for two more drinks.

"But I was wrong," he went on. "Paul brought back plenty of stuff—I expect he's shown it to you. Every time I saw him he had something new—gold, silver, copper—according

88

The Wai-ai

Notere's home

Notere—the headman

to him; once he said he had found platinum. Climbing about on those rocks was too much for him, and anyway the assay reports from Brisbane were disappointing." Petrie sipped his drink thoughtfully. "After a lot of trouble I persuaded him to stop. Before that I thought there might be something in crocodile skins for him. Paul's a wonderful shot, championship class, if you know what I mean."

"I've seen his rifle, a Mänlicher six-five with a telescopic sight," I said.

"Have you noticed how well he keeps it? Paul understands firearms. I got him that rifle and a thousand rounds of ammunition about four years ago." Petrie laughed. "After all that, we found there was no market for the skins. The dealers could get all they wanted from Queensland."

The boy came for empty glasses; it was my turn to sign for drinks.

"How can he be content with the life he leads?"

Petrie sighed. "I don't know; Paul lives in a dream world and gets bright ideas. He was going to make a fortune from turtle shell; any number of hawksbill come ashore on the sea-ward side of the island. I shipped a couple of hundredweight and got a fair price for him, but he lost interest. He had a go at *bêche-de-mer*, the big sea-slugs you cure in a special way. One shipment went wrong and he wouldn't try again. Then there were sharks' fins." Petrie tailed off inconclusively.

"Any chance of getting him home?"

Petrie shook his head. "He's got no people left, not a living relative in the world—anyway he'd see no reason for going."

We fell silent.

"It's a sad business," I said at last.

"Yes, it's tragic. One of these days I'll call at his place and find him dead. I shall be sorry, but it might be the best thing for him."

Petrie's friends came for him, but I declined to join them.

The south-east trades had ceased to blow. The north-west monsoon had followed, but now that was coming to an end

D

with calms, variable winds and sudden torrential rainstorms. The leaves of the yam vines had begun to turn brown, but the yams would not be dug for another month. After that it would be time to clear land for the new planting. The wild nut harvest would follow. There would be plenty of work until the end of the year, but in April men found time to make copra in off-lying islands and to dive for trochus shell on the reefs. Except for a few skilled men making canoes or netting fibre into fishnets, there were only women and children in the villages. I spent only half an hour at Vulavu and then headed across Thousand Ships Bay towards Ortega Channel. The day had started hot and still, but by ten o'clock there were gusts of wind from the north-west and a patch of dark cloud appeared in the sky. The wind freshened and blew fitfully until we entered the channel and anchored off Kaevaga; then it dropped and rain fell in torrents. It fell with unyielding force out of a pale grey sky unrelieved by a sign of blue or the form of a cloud. Gagi and Wesu lashed the for'ard and after screens and then unrolled the side-screens and hitched tie-ropes over the cleats along the gunwale. For nearly an hour I sat smoking miserably and trying to read, imprisoned in a cell of dripping canvas, waiting for the rain to abate.

There was movement on the starboard side. Someone was trying to force his way under the screen; his head appeared in the space between two cleats, but there was no room for his shoulders to pass and as he attempted to force his way through he strained on the canvas and ropes. "Wait," I shouted. I gave a flick to two of the tie ropes and Joel heaved himself on deck. His long wet hair was stuck down to his head and water running off his shining brown body dripped on to the deck. He looked awkwardly out of his element, like some strange marine creature which had clambered aboard. At best his strange dialect and impeded speech made him difficult to understand, but now, as he grimaced and gesticulated and spoke very quickly, I recognised only a few of the words he uttered. The crew and police were below; the drumming of rain on the awning and deck had drowned the sound of Joel's arrival. I called through the scuttle of the engine room, and Hiro, passing a hand over his face after sleep in the close impure air below, came forward and greeted Joel drowsily.

Joel had paddled across the channel to tell me Jardine was ill. We went over to the island in blinding rain and anchored off the remains of the wharf. I followed Joel as he hurried with the quick lope of a bushman through the rain up the overgrown path to the hut. I went beyond the partition for the first time and found Jardine lying on a truckle bed covered by a thin cotton blanket. The roof leaked in four or five places and part of the bed was wet. There were two cheap native trade-boxes on the floor, a chipped enamel wash-basin on a wooden stand and an upturned wooden case against the bed with a pannikin of cold tea and a plate of yams on it.

There was no net to the bed. Jardine had often boasted that the island was free of mosquitoes. His hand felt hot and I wondered as I gazed at him whether he was right. When I spoke he groaned and turned a pain-wracked face towards me. He was more emaciated than when I had last seen him; he was very ill. He made no reply to my greeting, but slowly drew the blanket away. I was shocked by what I saw. There was an ulcer on his right leg, round and two or three inches in diameter. His shin bone, white, streaked with blood, was exposed, and his leg as far as his groin was red and inflamed. He protested piteously when I told him I must take him to Tulagi Hospital.

Though he was in acute pain he showed embarrassment in his manner, perhaps because the formality of our relationship had been disturbed and an unsought intimacy had been forced upon us. For my part I found it difficult to support the fiction that he was anything but destitute.

We left at six o'clock to clear Thousand Ships Bay before nightfall. We put Jardine on a mattress on the cabin house, but as soon as we got away from the lee of the land the ship rolled dangerously and we moved him to my bunk. He groaned and prayed incessantly, until shortly after midnight he fell into a comatose state and I wondered if he was dying.

We were at the islands off Tulagi at daybreak and as we

went down the fairway I remembered the time I had brought Shelton to hospital.

Jardine put on his little hat when the orderlies came with the stretcher and carried him past curious natives on the wharf, through the cutting, to the hospital. I promised to see him before I returned to Tataba.

Jardine had been washed and lay in hospital pyjamas when I saw him next morning. One pyjama leg was rolled up exposing taut smooth skin above and below the white bulky dressing covering the ulcer. I sat by his cot for only a minute. He had been given morphia and mumbled incoherently when I spoke to him.

Crichton was focusing a microscope when I stood at the open door of his office.

"Hullo," he said. "Who's going to pay hospital fees for this old man?"

"I don't know. How is he?"

Crichton got down from his stool and joined me on the verandah.

"He's got a malignant ulcer, probably a yaws infection, and he is grossly undernourished.

"Will he get over it?"

"I don't know," Crichton said after brief reflection. "I don't know; I'll tell you in a month's time. He's pretty sick now."

When I returned to Tataba I toured the island on tax collection and it was two and a half months later, at the end of June, before I was again in Tulagi. I tied up at Government Wharf to load the quarter's stores and then, just before the office closed, I took surplus cash to the Treasury, bathed, changed and walked through the cutting to the Club. The place had seemed crowded when I arrived, with fifteen or twenty people sitting at tables on the verandah talking animatedly and calling for drinks, while the westering sun sunk lower in the sky over the sea. Then suddenly, but for two noisy men throwing dice on a corner table and getting steadily drunk, the place was deserted. Ah Sui wanted to lock up and go home. There was little time left for me to get food at Elkington's Hotel. A star-lit sky and a nearly full moon lighted my way along the path. Though I walked smartly and sweat formed on my brow, I found the balmy evening enchanting. Someone was playing a steel-stringed guitar in the *Wai-ai*. On the path down from the hotel two men slowly passed me; one was thin and more than six feet tall, his companion was short and thick set. Then the taller man spoke and I recognised the tone and thickness of Jardine's speech. I stopped and turned impulsively, but still with the formality we maintained between us, I called, "Mr Jardine."

He turned abruptly and exclaimed with pleasure.

"God bless my soul, it's Mr Fowler."

Moonlight lay across his face, and as he spoke I saw him closely. Lack of teeth gave his mouth a pinched appearance, but he was sleek and well fed. I had never seen him looking so well. His beard was gone, his hair was cut and carefully brushed and he wore new drill trousers and a shirt with two buttoning breast pockets and a tie. He shook my hand vigorously.

"How nice to see you," he kept on repeating. "How very nice to see you."

"I was going to visit you tomorrow," I told him when I got the chance.

He laughed. "I've been out more than a week."

"You are fully recovered?"

"Oh yes." He hopped a pace on his right foot. "I'm going to Ulawa tonight."

"You are going to Ulawa?"

"I thought you'd be interested."

He looked towards his companion.

"You know Andy?"

Andresen was a hard-working Swede with a trading station and small plantation. Everyone knew him. I took his outstretched hand.

"I ran into Andy as soon as I came out of hospital. He wants to go down to Sydney for a few months. I said I'd look after his place while he's away."

I was thrilled by his appearance and by what he told me.

"That's splendid," I said. "Don't hurry back. Look for another job when Andy returns."

He was not listening; he regarded Andresen with a benign and, I thought, a slightly patronising air.

"Andy must get away to Sydney for a spell," he said, as though recognising a duty towards him.

Early-morning haze stretched away over the discoloured water of the channel. Wesu stood for'ard with a lead-line calling soundings as I sat at breakfast. We were leaving Kaevaga to get outside the barrier reef ahead before fixing a west-north-west course for Furona Island. The echoing report of a rifle shot and the whine of a bullet came over the water and above my head there was a loud shattering sound. Something fell on to the awning and slithered over the canvas into the sea. I went aft and stared at the rigging; a block in the peak halyards was smashed and the gaff hung askew over the awning. A surge of furious anger choked me.

"Somebody's firing at us!" I exclaimed stupidly. " somebody's firing at us!"

Wesu lifted his chin towards the island.

"Mr Jardine."

"Don't be stupid, Mr Jardine's not here any more."

He pointed with a finger.

"Mr Jardine, see him."

"No, I can't," I said crossly, but I turned to Kepi.

"Over to the island," I ordered.

Kepi brought the *Wai-ai* round with a touch of the helm and we crossed the channel at half speed. As the grey sand of the waterside approached I saw Jardine standing by the tree above the beach near the remains of the old wharf. He raised his left arm when I got into the boat and Wesu and Gagi rowed me ashore. He wore frayed shorts cut down from trousers; his legs were bare, but there were socks and heavy boots on his feet. A white puckered hairless patch showed where the ulcer had been. I could see long hair under his hat and he had the beginnings of a straggling beard.

When the boat grounded he came forward with a rifle under his arm and exclaimed with gentle concern.

"Oh, I say, did I smash that block?"

I looked back at the *Wai-ai* when he spoke. The gaff had swung over to the port side and there was a tangle of rope on the awning. I spoke with a sudden spurt of temper.

"What the devil do you mean by firing at us? You might have killed someone."

Jardine looked mortified by my outburst.

"Oh, my dear fellow, there was never any fear of that."

"Well, look at the rigging."

He was very contrite.

"Oh, I am sorry, I only wanted to put a shot over the ship to attract your attention; I particularly wanted you to call."

"You attracted my attention all right."

He regarded me with anxious guileless eyes, uncertain what to say next. My annoyance sprung as much from disappointment at seeing his return to his old feckless existence as from anything else. I had thought he would never come back to the island. But it was impossible to be angry with him for long.

"There are some spare blocks on board; they'll soon fix that rigging," I said.

His face brightened immediately and he spoke with obvious relief.

"I'm so glad. Now, come to the house."

He went ahead along the narrow path with the rifle held in the crutch of his arm.

"I'm surprised to see you here," I said as I walked behind him. "I thought you might have stayed away a few more months."

"Oh, dear me, no, I didn't want to be away from my place all that time. I wrote and told Andy. Fred Hollebone's there now—he'll be glad of the money."

It was five months since I had last been ashore at the island. The tangle of undergrowth, creeper and self-planted coconuts had got very much thicker between the lines of planted trees. Twice, large monitor lizards, three or four feet long, stood in the path and moved only when we were almost upon them. Black-and-white hornbills repeatedly flew out with staccato cackling cries and a laborious rustle of wings. Ducks and fowls in all stages of growth swarmed round the hut. A banana tree, bent over, looked as though it might break under the weight of a stem of over-ripe fruit. Tiny fruit flies hummed in a cloud over two or three pineapples rotting on their stalks. There was a pile of sprouting coconuts at the side of the house.

Joel sat on the ground turning ivory-palm leaves over canes. There was a glint of welcome in the quick upward glance he gave me.

"We must repair the roof," Jardine observed. "Joel's just getting some new thatch ready, but it's all right today; there's no rain. Go in."

Light appeared through the roof where patches of rotten thatch had fallen away, and fungi was growing on some of the rafters.

"Do you mind if I finish this before we do anything else?"

Jardine became busy cleaning the Mänlicher rifle, working quickly and expertly and finally wiping the barrel with an oily rag. When he had finished he took the rifle away behind the partition and returned with a stone in his hand.

"Now I'd like to show you something."

"Yes, what's that?"

He handed me the stone. It appeared to have been chipped from heavy crystalline rock; in the light it emitted a silvery sparkle.

"What is it?"

"I'm not sure," he said indifferently. "It could be one of three things." He took the stone back from me. "It's interesting, but it's not really what I want you to see."

He went behind the partition again and returned carrying two lengths of rough-faced stone piping. They might have been formed by the emission of gas through molten rock. He looked at me triumphantly.

"What on earth have you got there?"

"I guessed you'd be surprised."

I put out my hands and took the stones from him. They were very heavy.

"When did you find these?"

"Last week, and there are plenty more where they come from."

I raised and lowered the objects again, wondering at their weight.

"What are they?"

He fell into a vein of musing regarding me with curious intensity.

"Do you know what I believe?"

"No."

There was portentous silence.

"Do you know what I really believe?"

I shook my head.

"No, what?"

"This rock structure indicates the presence of oil?"

A fowl fluttered up on to the floor boards and picked its way a few feet from us in search of a place to lay, and then a gaudy-hued lizard, chasing its buff-coloured mate, overran itself and fell flop on the ground outside. Jardine and I sat facing each other. I must have laughed, because his look of intensity passed and truculence came into his normally gentle face.

"Yes, oil," he snapped. "This island is of the same geological age and structure as the Dutch islands." He paused. "Now you know why I wanted to see you."

I searched vainly for words to divert him.

"You need immense capital to prospect for oil," I said weakly. "There are elaborate surveys and a lot of experimental drilling to be done."

"I know, I know." He spoke impatiently as though I were making unnecessary difficulties. "I've got to interest one of the big companies. I must prepare a report; I want books on the subject."

I was ashamed of my involuntary snigger, and with some idea of mollifying him I let the words slip out.

"I'll get any books you want."

I regretted the suggestion as soon as I had spoken. It seemed to make me a party to an insane enterprise, but there was no drawing back. Jardine's gratitude was excessive. He behaved as though a significant step had been taken and he spoke with great emotion.

"You won't lose by it, my dear fellow, I promise you that."

There was nothing more to say and I was conscious of anti-climax. Jardine had exhausted himself, but he stirred suddenly.

"Joel brought me two nice mullet and some sweet potatoes this morning. We'll have some *kai kai*."

"It's a bit early, isn't it?"

He walked to the edge of the room as though he had not heard me and leaned over the flimsy verandah.

"Joel, Joel!" he shouted. "Stop that now, come and cook *kai kai*."

My Sydney bookseller took four months to get books on oil exploration from America. There were four volumes, and when I took them to St George's Island, Jardine held them three feet away from his eyes so that he could read the print. He turned over the pages of each of them and then piled them up on the packing-case table at his side. The juxtaposition of these clean expensive books—they cost twelve pounds—with the squalor of the hut and the tattered illustrated papers on the floor had a disturbing nightmare quality.

Woodley had been gone a long time and Petrie had been away for eight months and there was doubt as to whether he would return again. I was now the only white man who ever saw Jardine. He was not constantly in my thoughts; I had other things to think about, but there were times when I felt burdened by a feeling of responsibility for him. I did not grudge the provisions I left him, they came out of my supplies and made little difference to my bills, but I was becoming exasperated by his requests for tools, drawing instruments, survey gear and stationery. He was petulant and incredulous when I told him that the things he wanted had not arrived and he could not understand that it took three months to get delivery from Sydney. I detected a veiled rebuke on two occasions when I arrived at the island without some article he had asked for. Once I suggested that he should make copra again. Though he could no longer ship to Tulagi by Petrie, a Chinese trader buying shell on the coast would call and barter provisions for it. He gave me a quick searching glance. "Copra," he said as though he had not heard me correctly, "I've got no time to bother with copra." I did not mention the subject again. He spent more and more of his time in the hills behind the plantation. If I had derided his activities as madness he might have stopped; but he was twenty-five years older than me and he was a gentleman, and I had grown to like him. Except when he had provoked me to anger by shooting through the rigging of the *Wai-ai*, my inclination was to humour him, although I was well aware of his folly. Moreover I was becoming convinced that events were taking an inevitable course, that Jardine's tragedy was drawing to its climax, and that there was nothing I could do to prevent it.

I anchored off Kaevaga in December. The weather had turned hot after heavy rain and it had been oppressive and humid ashore. I returned to the *Wai-ai* and started to sort out provisions—a twenty-five-pound bag of flour, two tins of sugar, a pound of tea, some tins of butter, condensed milk and corned beef. I put the provisions in a box and topped them off with an armful of old magazines. Gagi and Wesu were winching up the anchor when Hiro came to me. "Joel's coming," he said, and then I saw the canoe. I waited till it reached us and came alongside. Joel climbed aboard and spoke with breathless incoherency.

"For two day I no see Jardine," he mumbled.

Jardine sometimes took food and a blanket and spent nights in caves in the rocks. I was not immediately concerned.

"He take *kai kai* and a blanket?"

Joel shook his head.

"He not take *kai kai* and blanket this time; he say you come today; he tell me get pigeon for *kai kai* for you."

I recalled that I had sent a message along the coast to say I was coming and Jardine must have expected me.

I told Hiro to go back ashore and get as many men as he could. He returned half an hour later with only six. Jardine's disappearance had added to the old fear of the island, and even though they knew that I and the police would be there he could find only six men willing to cross the channel. We landed at the old wharf and walked in file up the path to the hut and beyond it through the derelict plantation for half a mile until we came to bush. Saplings, a few feet high, giant ferns and bamboo clumps in prodigal luxuriance crowded together at the foot of towering trees. Lianas and aerial roots, strong enough to bear the heaviest man, festooned the track, and, underfoot, fallen trees, rotten and fungus covered, sometimes barred our way. I frequently halted to tear off sticky cobwebs from my face and hair. Once we came upon thousands of white butterflies flitting like snowflakes against the surrounding foliage. Then the land became steep, rocky and bare. My three constables and I and the six Kaevaga men and Joel made a line about a hundred yards long and we toiled up the hill. There were folds in the rocks where earth had accumulated and where grass was growing and here the way was not so hard. Wetera was on my right and one of the Kaevaga men on my left. I had been climbing, sweating and breathless, for an hour; my heart thumped and there was a racing pulse in my temple. From where I stood, three or four hundred feet up, I could see over the wilderness of Jardine's plantation across the channel to the luxuriant verdure of the hills opposite. It was nearly four o'clock and we would soon have to turn back to reach the beach before sunset. A loud wail from Wetera stopped me in my tracks. He had forged ahead of me, and when I climbed up and came down into the fold in the rocks that he had followed I saw him coming towards me as fast as he could move over the uneven and rock-strewn ground. He would have gone past me without a word if I had not stopped him. "You find him?" I asked. He pulled away from me. "Let me go, master," he sobbed. "This place is no good." A wild animal terror beyond the appeal of reason possessed him. I let him go and walked on, bracing myself for whatever I had to see. Ten yards farther on a large rock partly barred the way but beyond there was a clear view for another fifteen yards. A narrow stream traversed the turf and stones of the hollow and flowed past a shapeless, ragged heap that I knew at once was all that was left of Jardine. Countless ants, like a brown undulating sheet, corroding and consuming, covered the body. An out-flung arm, stripped of tissue, lay white and bone naked; cheek bones and eye-sockets were exposed, and other parts of the body were hideously pitted. I felt in the presence of something diabolical and evil. A flood of horror engulfed me and I struggled with a compelling impulse to turn away from the place and run as far from it as I could. I recovered from the first frightening impact of the scene and went nearer. Jardine had broken his leg; there was a compound fracture of the right femur and pointed splintered bone pierced the partly consumed flesh of his thigh. A trail of bruised and bent grass led fifty yards uphill to a point where the grass gave way to boulders and where the sides of the hollow became precipitous. I saw where he had fallen. Twelve feet up on the bank there were signs of fresh digging and the pick I had brought him from Tulagi lay among the boulders below. A faded green canvas bag with a frayed edge that I had seen at the hut had been placed against a rock. In it was a prismatic compass, a notebook and pencil, a bottle of water and some bananas. Carrying the bag and pick, I retraced my steps down the slope. The police and the Kaevaga people stood waiting in a cowed silent group, but before I could reach them the men had torn off their *lava lavas* and had run away naked, slapping at their thighs as viciously-biting driver ants, spreading wide over the ground from the main stream, raced up their bare legs. I followed them down to the plantation and along the path to the beach. There was nothing I could do there.

Delayed shock from the horrors of the afternoon robbed me

of sleep. Joel, who had refused to leave me, spent the night in the *Wai-ai* sitting alone and inconsolable and making strange sounds like a sick animal. No one had the heart to silence him.

Next morning I went back to the island with the three constables. The ants had finished their work and there was a channel where they had moved off. We buried what was left of Jardine in three feet of earth, which was as deep as we could dig; and then returned to the *Wai-ai*.

We spent two more days at the anchorage. There was the inquest, though no one wanted to talk; and later I made a list of the contents of the hut. I took away the rifle and some of the things I had recently got for Jardine—I supposed I should be told what to do with them. I said Joel could take the rest of the stuff, but he shook his head and refused to touch it.

The light was too poor for us to leave by the time I had finished that second day. The village was silent and the police and crew moved about sombrely in the *Wai-ai*. The picture of what I had seen two days before in the hills was fixed for the time in my mind. It was midnight, but I still sat smoking and drinking with no feeling for sleep. Hiro, with a blanket draped over him, came and stood before me in the dim light.

"What d'you want?" I asked. "Can't you sleep?"

"It is better we never go ashore at that place again."

"Why?"

"Bolofaginia is angry."

I looked at him without speaking.

He shuffled his bare feet on the deck and hitched the blanket over his shoulder.

"Bolofaginia sent ants to kill Mr Jardine."

The cigarette end hissed when I tossed it into the water.

"Shut up, you fool, and go back to bed."

He stood obstinately, shadows lying across his face.

"Well?"

"It's true," Hiro said; and then, holding the blanket about him, he moved off silently into the darkness beyond the range of the lamplight.

CHAPTER FIVE

'Devil Devil' Man

IT was noon when I got back from the Russell Islands, sixty-eight miles south of St George's Island. I had spent three weeks visiting plantations. Tarova saluted and handed me a letter when I stepped ashore. It was two weeks old; Hever had signed it for Darcy. I was ordered to send the *Wai-ai* to Tulagi without delay. Lang warned me when I went in with Shelton that the vessel was due for a major refit. A Gardner diesel engine was on order for her and she would have to be slipped and probably some timbers replaced. I remembered all this when I read the letter. I must expect to be without the *Wai-ai* for six to eight weeks.

Next day I saw the *Wai-ai* go off with a sudden misgiving, heightened by the news that Kepi was sick. I had noticed in the Russell Islands that he had lost weight and that there were times when he sat abstracted and silent. There was an unhealthy waxiness in his complexion and his eyes seemed to have become big and round. I had not thought of him as ill until his unsteady gait and obvious weakness made him unfit for work. He protested as far as his good manners would allow, but I sent him to a hut near the barrack until the *Wai-ai* returned.

At first I did not miss the *Wai-ai*. A few idle weeks at Tataba were an agreeable change. But as the days went by I found nothing to do in the office, nothing at all—I had read all the books at the house—and I began to feel lonely and homesick. I found myself wanting something to happen, some variety, some occupation to immerse myself in.

I hung up a kit-bag packed with kapok and weighted with sand. I punched it night after night for two weeks, but my malaise was becoming too deep to find relief in this remedy. The period from supper to bedtime seemed endless, but when the ten o'clock drum sounded and I was half-heartedly rereading one of my books I was often too wakeful and restless for sleep. Mosquitoes came in through the sitting-room windows, buzzing round me and biting my ankles persistently. I slapped at them or moved my legs, but every night marks under my socks showed how badly I had been bitten. I suffered from chronic mild malaria and often felt heavy-limbed and sluggish, though not ill enough to lie down. I forced myself, morning and evening, to walk round the station. I went past the office taking the right-hand path to the end of the wharf; then I retraced my steps either by the path round Draper Point to the beach or the other way along the harbour side, skirting the mangrove swamp where crabs squelched on the edge of the blue-black mud and the amphibious creatures flipped across the dark pools. On morning walks there were prison gangs or police fatigue parties to vary the tedium of routine. Prisoners were planting the barren red hillside with casuarinas and digging drains to carry off storm water, and there were two Malaita men felling dead trees which still disfigured the scene. I watched one man each morning. He was a big man whom I had sentenced for wounding. He swung his axe rhythmically, engrossed in his labour, his beautifully muscled arms and torso glistening with sweat. When the tree began to fall he let out a loud shriek of achievement, dropped his axe on the ground and drew a hand across his sweaty face. An answering shriek came from the other prisoner and then the big man, after a brief pause, picked up and shouldered his axe and walked on to the next tree.

I spoke to Kepi every day; he was losing weight and growing weaker. I wished that I had allowed him to go to Tulagi with a note to Crichton. He complained of no pain; indeed, he seemed amazingly serene and his placid resignation was more disturbing than positive symptoms would have been. One day a canoe was beached on the sand near the hut. People from Vulavu had come to take him home. I demurred, doubting whether he was fit enough to travel. But four men stood waiting; and there was nothing I could do. One of the men carried Kepi's bed-roll to the canoe and another followed with a trade box and a lamp. Kepi gave me a shell; it was a black lip shell, similar to a large mussel shell, with an edge that was serrated like a saw. It was his spoon and a valued possession. I looked at him with surprise and told him to keep it. For a man so feeble he made a brusque gesture of refusal and walked slowly down the sand to the water. With confused feelings I watched as he got into the canoe and the four men paddled him away towards Martin Point.

There was mystery surrounding Kepi and his illness. Hiro was seated at his table outside my room when I returned to the office.

"What is wrong with Kepi?" I asked him.

He looked at me furtively without standing up.

"I don't know," he replied.

"You've not seen this thing before?"

"No, I've never seen it."

He spoke evasively, his voice slightly raised. I looked at him in silence and his eyes flickered under my gaze.

"You think Kepi will get over it?"

"No, I don't."

"You think he'll die?"

"Yes."

He withdrew into a state of aloof reserve. There was nothing to be gained by further talk. I passed through the door to my room and sat at the table more mystified than before.

I told Tarova to rebuild the barrack. With no escort duties with me in the *Wai-ai*, there was a danger of the police becoming idle. The barrack was not in a bad state, but to strip and rebuild it would keep the police busy, and the same opportunity might not occur again in the near future. They went into the bush behind my house and reappeared at the end of the day hurrying down to the beach with timber trimmed for poles, beams and rafters, with linias and vines for lashing, sago-palm leaf for thatching, and areca-palm wood for floors. This went on for two weeks, and on my walks I stopped to stare at the growing mass of material. I spoke to Tarova at the beach and asked him why so much was needed. I did not like him; he was not the punctiliously correct man that Dolimae had been. He was a lout, and some constables traded on his vanity. With a slight smile he looked at me speculatively before he replied.

"Me make big barrack this time," he said.

He gave a curious emphasis to the word big, and continued to smile.

"Why?" I demanded. "I told you to build a barrack like the old one."

"It is better we have a big barrack this time."

He spoke in a wheedling tone as though trying to impose his will. I was speechless with anger as a lot of old resentment welled up in me.

"You don't know what an order is? Suppose I tell you to do something, you do it. I don't want this talk talk."

Tarova was silent, abashed but not really chastened. As I turned away from him I saw a separate pile of material and new post-holes for a big house a few yards away from the barrack site.

I faced him again. "What's this for?" I demanded.

"It's for my house."

"Your house?"

"Yes, the police are building me a house."

He stood in an ungainly, relaxed posture. He was big for a Melanesian and his long bushy hair made him seem taller. For a moment I thought of ordering him to stand at attention, but I was not sure of my voice. I spoke quietly.

"Who do you think you are? About six months ago you get a corporal sash and now you want a house as though you were number one Sergeant-Major at Tulagi."

This time Tarova flushed and looked embarrassed. I followed up my advantage.

"You make a barrack like the old one and you do not build a house for yourself," I said.

I walked off feeling deflated. I felt relieved that I had emerged so easily from the conflict of wills.

An hour later Tarova came to the office in uniform. I wondered what had brought him since I had seen him at the beach. He saluted.

"Yes, corporal," I asked, "you want something?"

"Yes, sir," he said. "We won't build house for me and the new barrack will be as you say, sir."

He was like a child, I thought. He wanted to keep my good opinion.

"Yes, all right," I said.

He saluted and went out. Almost immediately Hiro came into the room and carried out the waste-paper basket. He looked smug, I thought.

When I came down from the house three days after my trouble with Tarova, Hiro followed me into the office. He had the preoccupied manner I knew so well. I felt a sudden presage of evil.

"Yes?" I said when I sat down.

He cleared his throat.

"I hear Kepi died last night," he announced.

"Who told you this?"

"Somebody from Vulavu took the news to Palukue and he told us."

"Palukue?"

"Yes, he was a friend of Kepi's."

Hiro was less withdrawn than he was when I had spoken to him about Kepi a week before.

"Speak the truth," I said firmly. "What is this sickness of Kepi's?"

He replied without hesitation. "They say he got *tatari*."

"*Tatari*, what you call *tatari*?"

Hiro cut off three inches of string from the ball on the table and made a loose loop.

"There are some old men who tie a piece of creeper or vine in this way. If they want to make anyone die they put this thing in the road where the man will walk, or on his bed."

He fell silent. I waited a moment for him to go on, but he remained silent.

"Is that all?"

"No, after the man has walked over the thing or lain on it, the old man takes it and pulls the knot tight like this." Hiro drew the ends of the string and tightened the knot. "He calls out the name of the man who is to die and prays to an ancestor's spirit. Then he puts the thing over a fire and smokes it dry. If he wants the man to fall ill he tightens the thing slightly; if he wants him to get better a little, he loosens it. When he wants him to die, he pulls the thing as tight as he can."

"Is this why Kepi has died?"

"So everyone says."

"Who did it?"

Hiro shook his head. "I don't know," he said. "There are old men who do this thing for money."

I was not satisfied, but for the moment I could think of nothing more to say and Hiro went to his place outside. He came back in a minute to say that Palukue was asking to see me.

Palukue walked slowly into the room. "I did not know Kepi was your friend," I said to him. "I am most grieved about his death."

Palukue was obviously under strain. He made no reply, but stood facing me, his face working with distress.

"There is some money due," I went on. "I'll pay his wife up to the day he died."

"You must give that woman nothing," he cried passionately. "She is wicked."

He had walked up to the table and looked at me imploringly.

"How is she wicked?" I asked.

"Before Kepi was dead she was already lying with another man," he said with loathing in his voice.

"Oh dear, oh dear, who is this man?"

"His name is Sule; he is a Vulavu man."

I broke the silence which followed.

"I am told Kepi died from sorcery called *tatari*," I said.

Palukue grunted as though in agreement, but I pressed him for a reply.

"What do you think?" I asked.

He paused, as though reflecting, and spoke weakly and with obvious aversion.

"That's what people say," he said.

"Do you believe it?"

"Yes," he murmured. "I don't understand it, but I believe some malevolent power was invoked against him."

He spoke the only English he knew, and even in his distress he was pompous.

"I'll send for this man Sule," I said.

Palukue looked horrified. "Oh no, better do nothing lest greater misfortune befall."

"Nonsense. If I can make the man tell us more, I shall do so, you can't run away from these things."

He gave me a quick look and seemed about to speak, but apparently changed his mind. I walked out of the office with him. The wind was blowing freshly from the north-west; I could see whitecaps out to sea beyond the reef. It was a cool pleasant day, but a spell of severe weather might follow. I told Hiro to tell Tarova I wanted Sule and Kepi's woman brought to me.

Four days after I had seen Palukue, I came down to the office to find Wetera talking to Hiro at the door. A man and woman waited under the mango tree. Hiro followed me into the office. "Constable Wetera has brought this man Sule from Vulavu," he said.

"Kepi's woman with him?"

"Yes."

"Tell them both to come in," I said.

I recognised the man when Hiro brought him in. He had worked for Chinamen in Tulagi and was now a middleman for them dealing in trochus shell. The woman stood at his side.

There was grace and elegance in her posture, but she had bedecked herself with too many porpoise-teeth necklaces and anklets. Unlike the man, she looked back at me fearlessly and untroubled. I spoke to her first.

"You Kepi's wife?"

"Yes," she replied without hesitation. She waited for me to speak again, but I turned to the man.

"They say you paid someone to make Kepi die."

He looked back at me with uneasy close-set eyes.

"It's a lie," he protested vehemently, but now he avoided my eyes and peered furtively about the room as though seeking a way to escape.

"You know how he died?"

Sule shook his head. "No, I don't know, why should I?"

I looked at him meditatively. He was obviously troubled and uneasy.

The woman turned from him to me, not understanding what had been said.

"All right," I said. "Maybe this woman knows?"

She was surprised but not anxious.

"He died from some sickness," she said calmly. "Nobody made him die."

I repeated the question to the man, but he continued to protest that he knew nothing of Kepi's death.

"If I knew that you had done anything to make Kepi die, you would hang, savvy? You would hang; you would die at the end of a rope."

He was now very frightened and looked as though he might run out through the open door of the office at any moment. He became steadier when the woman whispered to him, and from then on there appeared to be no hope of an admission. I said they could go, and Hiro escorted them out.

"That woman's a whore," he said when he came back. I let the remark pass, but he remained standing before me at the table.

"They say Sule went to an old man named Kile," he added.

"What did you say?"

"People say Sule talked to an old man named Kile."

"Kile, where does he live?"

"He lives at Regi."

I was depressed and frustrated. Much had happened about which I had not been told.

"Why did not someone tell me of this before?"

Hiro's eyes flickered and he looked away before he replied.

"Everyone's afraid of Kile."

"Are you afraid of him?"

"Yes."

"What! you are afraid of this man?"

Hiro's manner changed and he looked back at me stolidly.

"Kile can make a man die," he said. "Kepi died; someone else could die too."

"I'll see this man Kile tonight," I said firmly. "I'm not afraid of him."

I opened the cash book as a signal for Hiro to go, but he remained where he was.

"It is better for you not to see him," he declared tonelessly before he slowly went back to his place.

I walked briskly along the sandy shore path. It was the period called *na vula i rote* in the second half of the year when the canarium nuts mature, when *sokara lau*, the south-east trade blows and puddings are made from taro and newly harvested nuts. Pigeons swarmed in the leafy tops of heavily buttressed trees swallowing the fruit for its purple fleshy rind. Outside some houses long funnel-shaped baskets lay full of nuts to be smoked. On my way to Palukue's house I espied Hoile in the village and told him to come with me. He called through the open door and Palukue came out. His first look of surprise gave way to a wild, worried expression when I told him I wanted to see Kile.

"He's not here," he said hurriedly. "He's not here."

"What do you mean?" I asked.

"I can't take you to him."

"You're afraid?"

"I can't take you to him," he repeated miserably.

"All right, I'll find him myself."

"It would be better," Palukue said, "if you went back to Tataba."

I turned my back on him. "Find the house of this fella man Kile," I said to Hoile.

If Hoile knew where Kile lived, he certainly did not show it; nor did he make much effort to find out. A shrill old woman who overheard his half-hearted enquiries pointed to the house. Kile was sitting under the overhang of the roof. His emaciated old body was scaly and wrinkled; red-coloured spittle dribbled from the corners of his mouth as he tried to chew areca nuts. A lean underfed cur raised a cloud of flies as it got up snarling at us and then fled, yelping when a woman struck it with a stick.

Kile waved Hoile aside and fixed his rheumy old eyes on me. He could not understand what I said and Hoile interpreted as I slowly addressed him. I told him I thought he knew something about Kepi's death, but as soon as I had spoken I knew that my enquiry was futile. Kile rose unsteadily to his feet and, pointing at me with a forefinger, poured out what seemed to be a tirade of threats and abuse, in a voice which almost became a scream. Women standing near by looked towards us fearfully and then resumed the pounding of nuts and taro in their wooden food-pots. Hoile told me nothing of what Kile had said, and when I pressed him he protested that most of it was meaningless. He walked back ahead of me to the station.

At eleven o'clock next morning Hiro announced that Palukue was outside.

"What's he want?" I asked.

"I don't know," Hiro replied. "He says he wants to speak to you, that's all."

"Tell him to come in."

Palukue was nervous. He licked his lips and cracked the knuckles of his left hand. He looked at me with anxious eyes.

"What's wrong with you?" I asked.

He looked uneasily at Hiro.

"I want to talk secretly to you," he said.

"You want Hiro to go?"

He became more uneasy. "Yes," he said.

"Go outside," I said to Hiro. Then I looked expectantly at Palukue. "What d'you want?" I demanded.

It was the first time I had seen Palukue wearing a shirt tucked into his *lava lava*. It was a cheap striped flannelette garment which a Chinaman must have sold him. Palukue thrust his right hand through the front opening of the shirt and brought out a small gourd, three inches long and curved slightly at one end. A fragment of coconut husk was plugged into the hole.

"This is *poopono*," he said wretchedly.

His action mystified me. "*Poopono*, what's that?" I asked.

"You are in great danger, this will protect you."

"You've brought me a charm?"

"It's more than a charm; it's a kind of medicine."

I held out my hand. "Let me see it," I said.

With slight hesitation he allowed me to take the gourd. I removed the plug and raised the gourd to my nose.

"It's got ginger in it, hasn't it?" I asked.

"Yes, ginger and other things," Palukue said, his eyes fixed on me watchfully.

I poured some of the mixture on to the palm of my hand. There were pieces of bark and dried leaf in it. I sniffed it again, but only detected ginger.

"How do you use it?"

"When you are in danger, you eat some of it—you chew it with areca nut if you wish—then you spit in the direction from which danger approaches; after that you spit on your own body."

I put a little of the mixture in my mouth and chewed it; the taste was disgusting. "I should be sick if I ate this," I said.

"You wouldn't be sick," Palukue said earnestly. "You must take it."

I shook my head and handed the gourd back to him. "I don't think I need this," I said.

He was distressed. "You do need it, you are in danger," he insisted.

"In danger from Kile?" I asked. "No, he can't hurt me."

Palukue sniffed hard and drew the back of his right hand across his eyes. He fell silent, crestfallen and rebuffed. He took the gourd from me. "You won't tell anyone I offered you *poopono*," he said as he put it away under his shirt.

"No, I promise you I won't," I said.

I walked with him past Hiro's table to the outer door.

"Good-bye," I said. He looked about apprehensively.

"Good-bye," he replied, and without another word he hurried down the hill.

Hiro was weeding the grass near the mango tree. "Come back now," I called to him.

Six prisoners were still working on the hillside planting casuarinas, but the two Malaita men had finished felling the dead timber. One of them, the big man, was digging drains at the foot of the hill, the other, an unusual-looking man with the pound cipher and the figure five tattooed on a forearm, was painting my house. After twenty-five years of seafaring between Pacific ports, Fivepounds had returned to Tulagi with the battered visage of a pugilist, a sophisticated manner and in command of a language compounded of pidgin English and American and Australian slang. Most people liked him, but he was troubled by a young half-caste named Pallet who fancied himself as a boxer. In a scuffle on Tulagi wharf Fivepounds had thrashed him. He had overdone it and Pallet had complained to the police. Fivepounds offered no defence when he was brought before the court and he was sentenced to two months' imprisonment. Longman transferred him to Tataba prison where no one who knew him would see him in working gangs in prison clothing. As he painted the house I sometimes found myself drawn into conversation with him. He was a simple garrulous man. He told me of fights in Sydney at Rushcutters' Bay and with sardonic humour repeatedly related the story of a strange misfortune which had befallen him at Portland, Oregon. His drolleries amused me and I was glad to snatch at diversions as trifling as these in order to forget for a moment the burden of care which oppressed me. I had talked to him about painting door panels one morning and was wasting time before going to the office. Fivepounds failed to start a story about himself and instead gazed at me with concern. "You don't look good, boss," he said solicitously.

"I'm all right," I said. In a moment of weakness I added: "I'm just sick of having nothing to do."

"Why don't you get a canoe and go up the coast to one of white men for a few days?"

"They are too far away, and anyway I don't think I ought to leave Tataba."

"O.K., boss, you know best, I guess; maybe you ought to get yourself a girl."

I was wrong to talk to Fivepounds. He was a prisoner and his orders should have been given by the warder. But I thought him no ordinary man, and in the privacy of the house I persuaded myself there was no harm in talking to him. I did not rebuke him for his impertinence. "I don't think that would help," I replied.

"Well, I guess you know best, boss," he said; and as I left him and moved on to the office, he called after me: "Take it easy, boss, take it easy."

Two days after this conversation with Fivepounds I woke at daylight, earlier than usual and with a foreboding of evil. I slipped out of bed before Beni came in to put up the net. On the mangrove-stained floor boards between the bed and the door that led out to the earth closet there were dusty prints of bare feet. Someone had come to the bedside, turned, and had gone out. There was no mark of other movement in the room. I threw the hanging net over the frame and then I noticed the under-sheet lying loose over the mattress for a foot or eighteen inches. Nothing had been out of place when I had gone to bed the night before. I pulled more of the sheet away and a tendril of creeper fell to the floor. I stooped and picked it up. It was about four inches long and loosely knotted. It was still freshly green, though bruised by handling or perhaps by the weight of my body. I placed it on the chest of drawers. My actions were

automatic and independent of the horror which convulsed me.
I scuffed away the footmarks with my slippered feet, put the
scrap of creeper in a notebook and after I had shaved and
dressed went in for breakfast without a word to either servant
of what I had found.

Anyone who moved quietly could enter my bedroom from
the door at the back, but only someone indifferent to the
haunted banyan would dare to come to the house at night.
I had received a visit from Kile. I asked myself how many other
tendrils of creeper he had put in my way or under my bed. I
thought of him smoking a length of creeper over a fire, and
as he pulled it tight, shouting my name. Bugotu words all
ended in vowels. Sometimes I was called Fowla, but more often
Fowleri. Kile would shout 'Fowleri' as he performed the rites
of *tatari* and as he sought the aid of his ancestor's spirit against
me.

I took the notebook and after breakfast left for the office.
Fivepounds had finished painting in the house and had begun
to tar the supports below. He was late; I was half-way to the
office when I met him carrying a new drum of tar up the hill.
He greeted me before I spoke. "You certainly don't look good
today, boss," he said as he put down the tar. "You look crook
to me all right."

"I'm all right," I said shortly.

"O.K., O.K., that's fine," he said caustically, and took up
the drum.

Before he moved on I said: "Wait," he stood attentively
until I spoke. "Do you believe in this *tatari*," I asked.

Fivepounds put down the drum again and looked at me with
surprise.

"D'you take me for a bare-arsed bushman or what?" he
asked.

"You heard about Kepi, my bo'sun?"

"Sure, I heard about him. That was just too bad."

"You know how he died?"

"Sure, the boy was scared to death; he dropped his bundle."

"Maybe you're right," I said.

"You bet I'm right," he replied with conviction.

There was a brief silence, and I took out my notebook.

"Have you ever seen anything like this?" I asked, as I showed him the knotted tendril. He stared at it in surprise. His manner was defensive when he looked up and spoke.

"How come you have this?" he asked.

"I found it in my bed."

"You found this in your bed?" he asked incredulously.

"Yes, others may have been put in my way, but I have only seen this one."

I caught a glimpse of fear in Fivepounds' face. He remained silent.

"What's the matter with you?" I asked. "I thought you didn't believe in this sort of thing."

"I don't believe in it," he protested, "but everyone here says Kile's going to get you. Why don't you go away?"

A barrier had come between us. I could think of nothing to say to him. He picked up the drum of tar and mumbled something about starting work. I left him and went on my way to the office.

By nightfall I had become more uneasy, plagued by distractions which seemed to threaten my sanity. I found it impossible to relax sufficiently to read a book or write a letter after supper. I had been disturbed so often. On three successive nights small flocks of tiny birds had flown through the open window and then one by one had fallen down bruised and stunned by flying into walls. There had been nights when bats had circled the room incessantly. The flop of lizards dropping to the floor now sounded louder than usual. Large almost obscene-looking moths flew laboriously up to the lamp and sometimes they stayed motionless on the walls like ornamental plaques. There had been nights when the room had been infested by flying ants. A snake had moved across the bedroom floor towards me one night when I went to bed. I took an axe and cut off its head, but some reflex action kept its mouth opening and closing while the severed body curled up neatly a yard away. There was always something to rob me of tranquillity and repose. Later, in bed, I often found myself sitting up rigid with fright at noises I had never noticed before. A mysterious rustling, scraping sound had brought me out of bed one hot still night and with my torch I had seen six large land crabs crawling awkwardly across the gravel path. Roofing iron contracted with a sharp rat tat. Flying foxes from the banyan tree and nearby mangoes dropped fruit on the roof as they flew off, and some nights bull frogs kept up a hideous clangour making sleep impossible. There were other noises, strange and indeterminate, which I could not identify. When I did fall asleep my rest was spoilt by recurrent very vivid dreams and I woke up, sweating and exhausted, to another day of torment.

By day I lacked the energy to walk far and each afternoon I strolled aimlessly about the station. Sometimes I watched one of the police standing on a coral rock with a fish-spear. Tiny crabs on the beach scampered away in alarm as I approached. I stooped and picked up shells; there were large cowries mottled like birds' eggs. According to an island story an unspotted orange cowrie shell was valuable, but I never found one. I clutched at any slight variety in a scene which had become irksome in its familiarity. I knew every rock, tree and patch of sand on each side of the station paths; I had looked so often at the huts and station buildings that I had got sick of the sight of them.

The days dragged on and it became impossible to conceal from the people round me the sharpness of the homesickness and the torture of anxiety that had began to afflict me. It must have been obvious to everyone that something was wrong. I was sure they believed me to be the victim of *tatari*.

The crash of a falling tree was a common sound; I had often heard trees falling in the bush behind the house. I wondered one night at the crash and thud of a fall near at hand. Next morning I saw the tree. It was on the edge of the land surrounding the house. Its fall had been checked and it lay across the branch of another tree with its leafy crown spread over the ground but its earthy roots swung upwards pointing to the sky. At the office I gave orders through Hiro for prisoners to cut down and trim the fallen tree. Hiro remained where he stood. His arms hung limply at his sides and he appeared strange and unnatural.

"Somebody's going to die," he declared in a tone of sombre defiance as though he challenged me to deny it.

"Why do you say that?" I demanded uneasily.

"If a tree falls like that, someone must soon die."

"How do you know which way the tree fell? You haven't seen it."

"I've seen it," Hiro retorted. "Beni told me to come and see it and I went."

His lugubrious manner and his gloomy forebodings suddenly angered me. I spoke with asperity.

"You go tell the warder that I want prisoners to cut this tree as I have told you. If someone dies, he dies, but this makes no difference. Don't talk like a fool again to me. Now go."

With a perceptible effort Hiro drew himself up, turned, and went out through the door. Later in the day I surprised him staring at me with perplexity. In the following days when Tarova made his morning report and sometimes in the evening after he had lowered the flag, there was a barely concealed insolence in his speculatively smiling face as he uttered trivialities, standing before me ungainly and sloppy. I saw signs everywhere that I was losing my authority and I began to feel isolated and detached from everyone on the station. In the ominous expectancy with which I felt surrounded the daily routine seemed futile and I made little pretence at work.

On the Thursday morning of the sixth week after the *Wai-ai* had left me, I went down to the office and found the boss-boy from Foka Plantation where my friend Berryman was Manager. The boy had walked down with three labourers for me to pay off. There was a postscript to Berryman's letter. "Why not come up here for the week-end, I'm killing a beast on Saturday?" I thought of the purple yams, the dull boiled fish and the stringy fowls that

Beni offered me to eat. We had eaten fillet steak and sirloin the last time I had stayed with Berryman; I had travelled up in the *Wai-ai* then and it had taken me less than two hours. I reckoned it would take me five hours to travel by canoe to Foka. I wrote to Berryman to say he could expect me about noon on Saturday. During the night I lay sleepless and tormented by doubts. I wondered if I was taking a cowardly course and running away from something at Tataba. In the morning I wrote a second note to say I could not go to Foka; then I tore it up. I paid the police for the month and issued the weekly rations.

A canoe lay on the beach and Hiro and three other police were waiting when I got down to the barrack. It was low tide and the four men pushed the canoe through shallow water and one by one stepped gently in—two in front of me and two behind. Hiro had got me a *keda*, the light, easily handled canoe commonly seen round the south-east coast of the island. He sat in the bow and the three men behind took time from him and paddled through sheltered water to the reef. They quickened their dipping rate as they drew near to the passage and then Hiro abruptly exclaimed and stopped paddling. He looked over his shoulder and said something. The four men peered over the side. A large snake marked in black and white swam away from the bow of our canoe towards the reef; it was soon out of sight. The incident was over, I thought, but the men made no effort to restart paddling.

"What are you waiting for?"

"This snake," Hiro replied.

"It's gone."

His manner was sheepish and he spoke with a scarcely discernible smile as he looked back at me.

"It's gone, but it is better for you to go back."

"What are you talking about?"

He looked at the other men before he spoke.

"Maybe *devil devil* will get you, maybe the canoe will capsize and you will be drowned, maybe you will get sick and die. The snake is a warning for you . . ."

The canoe moved slightly in water sheltered by the reef; the four men rested with their paddle shafts on the gunwale.

"All right," I said with a sudden access of confidence. "That will do; no more of this nonsense. Start now."

Hiro spoke in an undertone and one of the men made a monosyllabic reply. The two others laughed nervously. Hiro was the first to dip his paddle, the rest followed and we went out to sea through the passage in the reef. Hiro rapped the gunwale with his paddle and all four men leaned forward, dipping as far ahead as they could reach and then making a long easy scooping stroke which propelled the canoe rapidly across the bay. As we pressed forward away from the station I felt an uplift of spirits and a sudden relief from the care and anxiety which had for so long oppressed me.

Hiro varied the stroke, signalling by a double rap on the gunwale for an alternative long and short stroke and during a short period for a stroke at double time. Off Fulakora Point we ran into the tide rip and the canoe plunged up and down, shipping some water. I baled with the calyx of a coconut until we reached the calmer water beyond. There was now a slight following sea and we made smooth progress along the coast on the seaward side of the reef. Hour after hour the four men paddled with tireless ease past clumps of coconut palms, huts, and stretches of sand. Smoke rose above the trees from land prepared for yam planting. Off one village people stood on the reef spearing fish in pools left by the low spring tide.

We beached the canoe in front of Berryman's house. Berryman was a tall fit-looking man with excellent features—a slightly aquiline nose, wrinkles at the corners of his eyes and a complexion bronzed by years of tropical sun. A large dog had gambolled about him while he waited, and when the canoe grounded came out towards us barking noisily. It ran ahead as we walked in the hot sun over grey-coloured sand. The house stood on ten-foot piles and on the ground below a carpet of cigarette ends, match sticks and bottle stoppers, weathered by sun and rain, blended into the dark background.

E

Berryman put two bottles of beer on a small table between us.

"I'm sorry it's not cold," he said.

I had slaked my thirst and we were lingering over the second bottle. "How are things on the plantation?" I asked. Berryman rolled, licked-up and lit his cigarette before he replied. I expected a non-committal reply, the usual lament at the low price of copra, but he said: "I'm worried about one of the labourers. He hasn't been out of the house since Lindstrom landed him three days ago. It costs twelve pounds a head to land a labourer here; we can't afford to have duds these days."

"What is he, a Malaita man?"

"No, Guadalcanal."

I was not interested, but Berryman seemed concerned.

"What's the matter with him?" I asked.

"I don't know; he's got no temperature and he doesn't complain of pain. He just looks to me like a man who's badly scared."

"He could be that all right," I said grimly.

"You've seen the same thing before?" Berryman asked in a worried voice.

"Yes, I've seen it."

"Can you do anything?"

"No, not as far as I know."

Berryman got up to get another bottle of beer.

"It's a bloody bad show," he said, "dumping a man like that on me. If he dies, I'll demand a replacement from Lindstrom."

Berryman pressed a lead pellet the size of a marble into the open twelve-bore cartridge. The bullock had been brought to a paddock near the house. Berryman shot it between the eyes at a range of ten feet. Three labourers rushed on the carcase with shouts, slashing at it with knives and an axe. The dismembered beast, surrounded by blood and filth, lay steaming on the sandy soil. Pele, the cook, cut out the tongue and took our joints to the house in a bucket.

We drank beer on the verandah until seven o'clock, then Berryman cut my hair and we bathed. The odour of an abattoir pervaded the house as Pele cooked and pickled meat in the kitchen. Berryman took away the empty bottles and returned with a bottle of whisky. "Distilled and Bottled in Scotland," he read from small print on the label to tell me that we were not about to drink whisky labelled "Distilled in Scotland" which we thought inferior. He slowly turned the bottle upside down three times to disperse the fusel oil, then he poured a little whisky away over the verandah edge and handed me the bottle. The ritual of whisky drinking in the Solomons had been observed. While we drank we rolled and smoked cigarettes without ceasing, tossing fag-ends and match sticks over the verandah to add to the accumulation on the ground below.

It was late when we ate, and nearly eleven o'clock when, gorged with rich food, we returned to our chairs. The big Alsatian lay at our feet beating the floor with a paw as he scratched at flea bites or wagging his tail and barking half-heartedly in his sleep. At half-past twelve, when Berryman opened the second bottle of whisky, the dog scrambled awkwardly to its feet and ran to the top of the verandah steps barking furiously into the darkness. "Come back, you fool," Berryman shouted. Still holding the whisky, he went to the top of the steps. The plantation boss-boy was standing outside.

"What's the matter, Tom?" Berryman enquired.

"This new chum sick too much; better you come, master," he said.

Berryman came back and put down the bottle. "It's that labourer I told you about," he said. He took the lamp and entered the room behind us, crossing to his little office on the back verandah. He returned with quinine, aspirin tablets, some other drugs and a thermometer. "When in doubt treat for malaria, they always say," he said. He stood for a moment holding the lamp. "Coming?" he asked. I followed him down the steps. Twenty yards away the sea was lapping on the beach.

"I haven't seen a tide as high as that before," Berryman said as we walked towards the thatch copra sheds and drier. Five of the labourers' huts were in darkness; from the sixth, the one nearest the sheds, a weak light appeared, and as we drew nearer I heard the sound of weeping. There was infinite despair in the sound, something inconsolable and dreadfully sad. There was a suffocating stench when we stooped and entered the hut. Three men were crouching round a fourth man who was on the ground. The two nearest made way silently for us. Berryman felt the pulse of the sick man. He stopped weeping, sat up and stared straight ahead as though terror-stricken, then he threw himself down on the ground in a frenzy. The three men held him and he stopped struggling and sat up, looking round the hut as though surprised but no longer frightened. Then he collapsed onto his back with outflung arms. Berryman picked up his wrist and put a hand over his heart. "He's dead," he said.

I took the moist limp wrist. I felt nothing, but I shook my head. "No," I said. "Leave him; he's sleeping." Berryman looked at me doubtfully. I nodded towards the opening, "Come on," I said, "let's go."

The cool land breeze was refreshing after the fetid atmosphere of the hut.

"What do you think we ought to do?" Berryman asked.

"Leave him," I said. "Put a blanket over him and tell those boys to go away."

"You hear what master say?" Berryman asked the boss-boy.

"I hear," he said, and went back into the hut.

The boss-boy rejoined us.

"You know this sickness?" Berryman asked him.

"I don't know this sickness."

The boss-boy spoke decisively, as though wishing to absolve himself from any connection with the affair; then, seeming to relent, he added, "His brother say one *devil devil* at their place called *vele* caught him before he signed for Lindstrom. A bright light shone at him in the bush one night and he was pricked all over with a spear fish."

Berryman was about to speak, but the boss-boy called one of

the natives who had been in the hut. He came unwillingly and faced Berryman with a dull uncomprehending expression.

"Is it true a *devil devil* called *vele* caught your brother?" Berryman asked.

The native looked wretched. He was barely audible when he spoke. "Me no savvy," he quavered in a faint voice, "me no savvy."

"He's scared," I said. "Leave it until the morning. You'll get nothing out of him tonight."

We walked back along the sand a few yards above the high water. In the bright moonlight there was no need for a lamp.

Berryman came into my room with a cup of black coffee. It was seven o'clock and too early, I thought, to be up after our late night. He was very cheerful. "That boy's better," he said. "I've just been down to see him; he was sitting outside his house eating rice. It's marvellous." He lit a cigarette and walked about the little room. "Drink your coffee and get up," he said. "I want to show you something."

I put on slippers and followed him down the steps and under the house.

"What do you think of that?" he asked looking at the sandy ground.

"What?" I asked.

"Those marks."

"They're crocodile tracks!"

"Come over here," he said.

He showed me where the tracks came from the high-water mark in front of the house and then went round the house. They passed the bottom of the steps, then crossed twice under the house and went back into the water.

"That was a big crocodile," I said.

"About eighteen feet long, I reckon," Berryman replied.

A heavy sea was running when I looked out on Monday morning. Spray flew high into the air as surf crashed into the reef in front of the house. Berryman joined me on the verandah.

"You can't go out in a canoe in that," he said. "Stay another night and go back tomorrow."

There was no compelling reason for me to return to Tataba that day, but the week-end was over and it seemed right for me to go.

"No, thank you," I said. "I'll walk."

"Walk! it's fifteen miles. Why don't you wait a day."

I suddenly felt quite sure I ought to go. "No, I must go," I said.

Three constables remained with the canoe and I started back on foot with Hiro. The path across the plantation round the bay was flat, but the way was sandy and walking was laborious. At the boundary we waded a river and climbed up over a point by a path festooned with lianas and vines and barred by strong cobwebs. Tree tops swayed in the wind. The north-westerly had freshened but the air was still where we walked shielded by thick bush and there was a horrid stench of corruption. Hiro just ahead of me, without lessening his pace, snapped back twigs which might have brushed against me.

The path tunnelled through the bush, descending to villages on the coast then rising again to high land beyond. At the fourth village I rested. We went to the canoe-house and I sat on the edge of a big canoe in the shade. There were five smaller canoes there; a fish net was suspended from the rafters and someone had dropped a spear on the ground. Naked children soon found us and stared steadily at me with unblinking gaze, When I feinted as though to grab one of them they scattered, falling over each other in their haste and shouting with laughter. They reassembled, chattering freely and occasionally bursting into laughter at remarks of their own. A youth of sixteen joined them and spoke to Hiro.

"Fetch the headman," I said.

The youth went off and returned with a man about sixty.

"I did not know you come," the old man said quietly through Hiro. He looked at me with greater respect than I was used to.

"No matter," I said. "You think we can go out by canoe?"

The old man shook his head and looked out to sea. "Sea too strong now; tonight might be all right," he replied.

I took out my tobacco tin. The cigarette papers and tobacco were dry, but the matches were sodden. I rolled a cigarette and asked for a match. The youth fetched me a glowing ember. There was silence as I puffed at my cigarette until the headman spoke through Hiro.

"You like anything?"

"No, thank you," I replied.

"You like green coconut?"

"Yes, I would like that."

The old man spoke and the youth went into a hut and reappeared with a small loop worked from creeper. He gave it a twist and passed his feet through as he stood at the foot of the palm. He gripped the trunk with hands and feet then, pressing on the trunk with the loop, reached higher with his hands, drew up his feet and repeated the motions until he reached the crown of the tree. He threw down two green coconuts and then descended. The headman slashed off the top of one of the nuts and handed it to me and I drank the tepid sickly fluid inside.

The journey became more and more trying. By midday I was so exhausted that I found it difficult to move at all; climbing a hill was agony. Two hours later we came to the open flat land round Fulakora Bay and I moved forward mechanically, feeling less distressed. At Regi dogs came at me snarling, and Palukue, moved by some lively emotion, rushed towards me with three other men following. My wish now was to get to Tataba, but I was compelled to stop.

"Welcome!" Palukue said ceremoniously.

"All right," I replied, regarding him with displeasure. He stood with the other men obstructing my way with unusual lightheartedness of manner.

"What's the matter with you?" I asked.

"You are a man of invincible *mana*. Kile is dead," he proclaimed.

A crowd began to gather round us.

"Kile dead?" I asked with surprise. "When did he die?"

"On Saturday morning he went into the bush and hanged himself."

I gasped with horror.

"Hanged himself?"

"Yes, he said you would never leave Tataba alive, but you defied his power and were not daunted by the warning snake."

I saw Palukue's glowing face and the admiring circle round me, but I felt no triumph in the death of the old man. It was as though I had been told about a stranger. Before I could speak, Palukue spoke again.

"You were too strong for the *vele* from Guadalcanal; everyone is talking how you forbade the man to die at Foka."

I turned to Hiro. "Is this true?" I asked.

His mouth turned down at the corners in a smirk.

"That's what they say."

"You believe it?"

He laughed with pleasure. "Yes, I believe it,"

Everyone was laughing gaily now. Palukue, bright eyed and excited, spoke again.

"You are a person of great *mana*; you are favoured by your guardian spirit. You are too powerful for these evil people."

"All right," I said. "I must go now."

The crowd opened reluctantly and allowed us to pass. It was five o'clock when I walked along the croton-bordered path in front of the barrack. Tarova came out and intercepted me. He was in uniform and saluted me.

"Everything . . ." he started to say, and then I noticed he was eating.

"You are eating," I said angrily. "How dare you?"

He turned to the side of the path and masticated rapidly.

"Everything . . ." he started again.

"You are still eating," I said. "Empty your mouth."

He went to the grass at the side of the path and spat. He came back and stood before me ungainly and relaxed. Before he could start to speak again, I said: "Stand up properly when you speak to me." He stood at attention.

"Everything all right while you are away," he reported. "*Wai-ai* come back . . ."

I cut him off. "When?" I demanded.

"Three o'clock, today, sir." he reported.

I hurried round Draper Point, my weariness forgotten. I saw her at the end of the wharf. She had a new green canvas awning and her fresh white paint gleamed in the afternoon sun. As I drew nearer I saw her polished brass and shining varnish. Soge looked grave when I spoke of Kepi, and Wesu and Gagi stood behind him mournful and sad. But the news had quickly reached them in Tulagi and the first shock was long past. Soge grinned as he showed me the ship. The big diesel engine was installed amidships, giving me a bigger room aft with two drawers under the bunk. I inspected everything; the smell of fresh paint, varnish and pitch and the sight of the gleaming new engine filled me with delight. She was like a new ship. I was loath to leave her. I stood on the deck, almost in a trance. "Mail-bag at the house for you, very heavy," Soge said.

I struggled up the short steep hill to the office and half-way up the second hill I met Fivepounds, walking slowly down from the house. It was half an hour after lock-up and he should have been in the prison. He turned and walked straight at me in the middle of the path.

"You're back, boss," he said excitedly.

"Yes," I replied, displeased with the familiarity of his manner.

Fivepounds was gleeful. "He's through, boss; he's all washed up," he declared, shaking with laughter.

"What are you talking about?"

"Kile, boss, Kile: he's dead, he's finished. He strung himself up in the bush."

Fivepounds' exuberance aroused no response in me. I had nothing to say to him as he waited eager for talk.

"Yes, I hear Kile died," I said. "I'm sorry."

He stared at me open-mouthed with surprise. When he saw I was not being jocular, he looked away in embarrassment and walked on. I thought as I went on my way to the house that I should be glad when Fivepounds' sentence was finished so that I could send him back to Tulagi.

Smoke came from the kitchen chimney. Beni had rushed up the hill and had lit the fire. I bathed, changed into pyjamas and sat down with a tea tray on a table at my side. There were two parcels of books in the mail-bag, many papers and magazines, and more than a dozen letters. It was a splendid mail. After the first quick reading I left the letters littered on the floor and table and went out to the verandah. I gazed down at the *Wai-ai* tied up at her berth. I felt elated; the past eight weeks of morbid fears seemed unreal and without substance—a nightmare from which I had awakened. I went back and read my letters again.

CHAPTER SIX

Off Course

I SAT on the bench and waited. A hard shaft of sunlight cut through the gloom of the court. It was late afternoon, but not too late, I thought, for me to finish the case.

Hiro touched the woman's arm and pointed, then he spoke to her and with a sleeping infant tied on her back she stepped hesitantly up into the dock and looked nervously round. She stood there, her body deformed by heavy work and frequent child bearing. Her husband, undersized and vindictive looking, was in the witness-box; he had brought a complaint of adultery against her.

In the old days the penalty for adultery was death; now in place of that offenders could reckon on a fine of five pounds or three months' imprisonment if they were found out.

The woman before me had confessed adultery to her husband and in a whisper she pleaded guilty when the charge was read to her. She had left her infant with an older child in the village and had gone alone to the garden. A man had come upon her there, and if she had not told her husband what had happened then he would never have known. He had brought his complaint to the court to be dealt with according to law, and in spite of the woman's plea I had to be sure they were properly married.

"How many years since you married this woman?" I asked the man. He discussed the question with Hiro and I waited for an answer.

"Eight years," he said.

"How did you marry her?"

The answer came slowly and it seemed almost unwillingly. "My father paid this woman's people."

The interrogation went drearily on.

"How much?"

"Two hundred porpoise teeth and five string red feather money."

I wrote down his answer and asked: "Anything more?"

He looked suspiciously from me to Hiro.

"My mother gave her yams to start a garden," he said.

I looked up. "You?" I asked.

"I gave her three calicos."

I turned to the woman in the dock.

"You hear what he said?" I asked.

Hiro patiently explained to her and she inclined her head but said nothing.

"True what he say?"

She gaped and looked at Hiro with dim comprehension. He explained the question to her slowly.

"His people paid," she agreed woodenly.

She would be well fed in prison. Her infant would be with her, and she would do only light work. She would rest there.

"Three moon for woman's prison in Tulagi," I told her.

She made no sign of understanding when Hiro explained. She began to pick her nose and to gaze round the room. Police led her away and I got down from the bench and followed them outside. People from the village were waiting there; the squalid little affair meant something to them.

The police led the woman towards the path down to the barrack. Until then perhaps the proceedings had not penetrated her understanding. With a sobbing cry she broke away from the two constables and blindly, with hands outstretched, she rushed to her husband. He swung his right fist at her and by an accident of timing it struck her hard on the chin. She fell without a sound flat on her face and her cloth ruckled up, exposing a buttock. The child on her back was unharmed but it cried loudly, roused by the fall. The man's face bore a doubtful expression of mixed shame and of satisfaction; he looked about

132

to see how the bystanders had taken his action. Hiro shook him roughly when he hustled him away from the court precincts. I went to my table in the office and wrote out the prison warrant for the woman. I gave orders for the *Wai-ai* to leave that night with her for Tulagi; there was no place at Tataba for her.

I went to bed early to escape the mosquitoes, and when I had finished reading, I lifted the mosquito net and put my book on the chair. I turned down the lamp and pressed the trigger to extinguish the flame. I felt under the pillow for my torch and then tucked the net under the mattress again. I could hear a mosquito buzzing round my head, but I was too sleepy to care. Soon afterwards, or so it seemed, I felt myself drawn up unwillingly from a deep well of sleep. There was a noise; someone was banging the gauze-covered door to the verandah. Not many people would come up the hill to the house at night; but now someone had come, and I was curious.

"Who's there?" I called out sharply as I switched on my torch and pressed it against the net pointing at the door.

"Me, Constable Hiro," was the reply.

Hiro spoke diffidently, as befitted an intruder into my house at night, or perhaps he feared the banyan tree.

"Yes, what is it?" I asked.

"Corporal Tarova say Toga is very sick."

I got up and pulled slacks over my pyjama trousers, pushed my feet into slippers and walked out to the verandah. Hiro stood there holding a hurricane lamp. The temperature had fallen during the night and he had draped himself in a blanket.

"What is the matter with Toga?"

"I don't know."

"All right, go on."

He walked a few yards ahead of me with the lamp. A cock, astir for a few minutes in the false dawn, crowed twice and then was silent. The moon in its first quarter cast a pale light over the station. A breeze off the land came in refreshing gusts, stimulating in the cool night air. On the reef the surf broke as with a laboured movement lacking force.

We had reached the office. "Is Toga like Kepi?" I asked.

"Ah," Hiro gasped. "I don't think so."

We descended the second hill to the beach. Hiro left the path and walked diagonally across the grassy parade ground to a hut near the barrack. A group of constables, like ghostly figures, stood silent near the entrance. Inside a poor light came from a glass-smoked hurricane lamp and someone had misguidedly lighted a fire on the ground. In the gloom I discerned the bulk of Tarova bending over a prone figure. Toga lay there breathing with rapid shallow breaths. His body was hot and dry; the stench of faeces came from his blankets.

"Can he talk?" I asked Tarova.

"He's too sick, he can't talk," he said.

I put a thermometer in his arm-pit. "How long has he been sick?" I asked.

"Two or three days; tonight he lay on his bed, very sick, he shit blood and was unable to stand up."

I took out the thermometer; it registered 105 degrees. There was not much I could do for Toga as he lay there. I told Tarova to have him gently moved to a better-ventilated hut when the sun was up and have him washed with warm water. I said I would see him in the morning.

I dropped into a deep sleep when I got back to my bed and I woke late, unable for a moment to name the cause of my anxiety. Then with dismay I remembered Toga.

"How's Toga?" I asked Hiro at the office door.

"A little better."

I was pleased to hear this.

"He talk?"

"He has talked a little."

"He drink or *kai kai* today?"

"He drink coconut milk."

At nine o'clock I went down to see him. His temperature was lower and he answered when I spoke to him. I told his friend Wetera to stay with him to see that he moved as little as possible. I sent down strong disinfectant for the sanitary pail.

For three days Toga's condition was unchanged; then he was

suddenly worse. During a few minutes when Wetera was absent he had somehow got up and had walked into the sea. He had collapsed on the beach on the way back. I was roused again that night and I went down to see him. But there was nothing I could do and I felt at my wits' end. I had reproached myself for not doing more for Kepi. If I had sent him to hospital he might still have been alive. I cursed the people in Tulagi for detaining the *Wai-ai*. She had been away four days after taking in the woman prisoner. The ship appeared the following afternoon and I gave orders for her to leave with Toga for Tulagi Hospital next morning.

I was down on the wharf when she left. Six constables carried Toga, muffled up with blankets on his bed board. His wife, carrying a few possessions, followed them with her infant. They put him down gently on the deck and lowered the side screens to shelter him. Wetera and the woman sat near. I spoke to Toga before the ship left. "Now you go for hospital, Toga," I said, "you will soon be better and soon come back." He turned on me a look of such intense reproach that I faltered in my speech. I walked away from the wharf and climbed the hill hoping I had acted for the best.

For months without respite I had been travelling the coast of the island, day after day anchoring at villages where people came alongside in canoes and clambered aboard with their tax money and with their requests and complaints. I had settled their disputes ashore and had sometimes held court. For a time —three or four weeks—there was no need for me to travel.

Two days after I had sent Toga to Tulagi I was reading idly in the office when Hiro came in to say that a Chinaman was outside.

He was a clean little Chinaman wearing faded denim trousers, a striped collarless shirt and slippers without heels. His schooner had come into the anchorage the night before. I looked at him with interest, glad of a slight diversion.

A native followed him in awkwardly carrying a long wicker chair with a connected leg rest, shaped for comfort. In the left arm there was a receptacle for books and in the right arm a ring for a glass. It was quite new and clean.

It was a better chair than the cane chairs issued to the house. I found it comfortable when I sat in it.

"How much?" I asked.

"Three poun'," he replied.

We haggled for nearly an hour. The Chinaman simulated indignation, amusement and impatience. He finally gestured to the native to take the chair away. He followed him out, but turned round suddenly and said: "One poun' ten."

"One pound," I said.

He called crossly to the native to bring the chair back.

"Allight, give me one poun'," he said.

I handed him the money and they left the chair. Hiro came in and stared at it. I told him to take it to the house. When I went up for lunch I placed it lengthways against the wall under the windows of the sitting-room. At tea, with a tray on a stool at my side, I gazed down at the irregular line of white breakers, and at night, when I put down my book, I peered through the open window into the purple humid darkness outside. I was pleased with my purchase.

After supper next day I settled myself in the new chair with a cushion behind me to read until bedtime. After the nine o'clock drum roll I counted the hours to be sure of the time. At a movement on my right ankle I involuntarily shook my foot and immediately I felt a sharp prick above the Achilles tendon of my right leg. I sat up abruptly and saw a centipede moving vertically down a leg of the foot-rest. It was seven or eight inches long, greenish in colour but turning to yellow on its underside. I was filled with horror before I was conscious of pain; a dreadful mishap had befallen me. I stood up. The centipede with its long undulating body was moving away. I stamped my heel on it and left three or four inches of tail wriggling convulsively adhering to the mushy pulp on the floor. I felt sick and walked with arms outstretched feeling my way along the back verandah to my bed. I pulled the net away and lay down. Spasms of pulsating numbing pain increased to a crescendo of unbearable agony and I started to retch violently. I stood up and walked shakily out to the front verandah. When the retching ceased I returned to the bed. My leg seemed awkward and big, but I slipped off my trousers and felt swelling only round the place of the bite. I took the torch from under my pillow. There was a lot of inflammation at the back of my leg. I expected this, but I did not expect to see the livid red streak pointing up the inside of my leg to my groin. For a moment fear numbed the pain I felt. I put the torch away and fell into a drowsy stupor.

Beni was in the room when I awoke. He looked bewildered as he put up the net and Atiu, drawn by unusual circumstances, stood agape by the door.

"A centipede has bitten me," I told them. "Bring tea."

The pain, though still acute, no longer came in sickening waves, and the streak up my leg looked less alarming in daylight.

Beni picked up my trousers from the floor and went out. Atiu brought me tea half an hour later. Soon afterwards the house seemed full of people. Hiro and Tarova were at the bedroom door and Beni came in and told me Palukue and another man were there too.

"What do they want?" I enquired wearily.

"There's a man with medicine," he said.

"All right."

"They can come in?"

"Yes, all right."

A feeling of apathy possessed me; I was resigned to suffering until the pain wore off. Hiro and Tarova looked at me with concern. Palukue fussily tried to say something, but I could not listen. Then Hiro spoke. "This old man brings medicine for your leg," he said and, as he spoke, he turned towards an elderly man standing awkwardly alone near the door. The old man brought out two large angular cone-like fruits from the fibre bag slung over his shoulder.

"Yes," I said, and they all went out. When they returned the old man carried a mash on a leathery looking leaf. I turned on my stomach and the old man applied the mash and the leaf to the bite. Hiro bound them in place with a handkerchief. Two hours later the old man made a fresh mash and put it on my leg. In the afternoon I felt well enough to get up for tea in the sitting-room. I told Beni to put the new chair under the house. I sat in the old cane chair set back in the centre of the room.

After Atiu brought in a lamp at sunset and one of the boys was pouring out hot water for my bath, a diesel engine exhaust sounded faintly over the water; it could only be the *Wai-ai*. I stood on the verandah and with my glasses I sighted the port light as the ship passed Martin Point. I bathed and dressed without haste. Her starboard light appeared now as she came round the marking buoys to the anchorage. There was nothing I could do to hasten the arrival of news, and I sat impatiently trying to kill time with a book until Beni came into the room.

"Wetera has come," he announced, and Wetera came blinking into the lamplight. His *lava lava* was creased and he looked strained and tired but he stood upright at attention when I spoke to him.

"You come back Wetera?" I asked.

"Me come back," he said.

"Toga?"

"He die."

"I'm very sorry," I said.

I had half expected to hear what he had told me, but I retained a hope that Toga had taken a turn for the better.

"When did he die?" I asked.

"Last night; this morning the police buried him."

Wetera was waiting for me to dismiss him. "All right, Wetera," I said, "you go now."

"Doctor send a letter," he replied as he opened the pouch on his belt. He handed me the crumpled envelope, saluted, and left by the back of the house.

I tore open the envelope; it looked a hurriedly written letter.

"*Dear Fowler*, I read. "*Your policeman was comatose when he was brought here. He should never have been moved. The chances are that he would have died anyway, but the journey in here made it*

138

certain. I don't want this hospital to get the name of a place where people are brought to die. I have enough trouble without that. Kindly show better judgment in future." It was signed: "*Alexander Crichton.*"

The effect of the letter on me was brutal; my feelings were lacerated. I dropped the sheet of paper on the floor and sat motionless, horrified at the thought that I had perhaps been the cause of Toga's death. My vitality was enfeebled by the centipede bite. With strange clarity I repeatedly pictured Toga's reproachful face. Beni looked at me curiously after he announced supper; I had evidently not heard him the first time. I wanted nothing to eat. My leg ached and I went to bed thrashing about restlessly but finding no relief, and during sleepless hours I thought only of Toga and of Crichton's letter.

Uneventful days followed. Much of the time I felt weighed down with inertia, out of condition, and lacking energy. One morning I sat at my table in idle abstraction. Hiro was outside weeding the grass round the office. With an effort I opened the cash book and applied myself to the monthly accounts. Then Hiro suddenly shouted "Sail Oh!" and came in and said that the *Tulagi* was in sight. I went outside and recognised the lean hull and raking masts of the schooner. She was an hour away, I reckoned, and there was time for me to decant some whisky, fill a box with cigarettes and change my clothes. Darcy was given to surprise visits; special preparations for prearranged visits displeased him.

The *Tulagi* was now coming round the reef to make the passage into the harbour; the Resident Commissioner's pennant was flying from the top of her tall after-mast. There was a loud blast on a conch shell then one of the crew stood in the bow with a megaphone. "Clear the wharf, clear the wharf," he shouted, but the customary command was unnecessary as Soge had already moved the *Wai-ai*.

Darcy was in excellent humour and made his usual observation as he stood on the wharf with me and gazed round the harbour and up at the house. "If I had the chance I'd change jobs with you," he said. He wore well-cut white drill trousers, white buckskin shoes and a white linen shirt. "Come aboard and have some tea," he said after we had walked the length of the wharf and back.

After tea we went up the hill to the office and he looked at my accounts and read my court records. We walked across to the prison and he complimented me on the fence. He asked to see the prisoners' warrants and then enquired if there were any complaints. He inspected the police; two of the men he spoke to were speechless with nervousness. He declined to come to the house and instead invited me to dine with him in the *Tulagi*.

I told him about Toga, the centipede bite and Crichton's letter. I was conscious of his sympathy. There was a gentle murmur of water between the schooner and the wharf and it was a cool night. I found myself sitting there relaxed and at ease with Darcy. We had been talking about cricket, when he abruptly changed the subject.

"How is your health?" he demanded.

"Oh, fairly good, I think," I replied without a thought.

"Do you eat well?"

"My food is often pretty disgusting, but I don't starve."

"Sleep well?"

"Not so well since my leg's been aching."

Darcy said nothing for a moment. He pressed a bell and his steward set down a tray of drinks between us.

"I am supposed to be going to Ong Tong Java next week, but it is not very convenient for me. You've never been there?"

"No, sir."

"I'll include Ong Tong Java in your district temporarily, and I think you'd better go for me."

"Yes, sir."

"You can have my interpreter Mareo, and you'll find it interesting. The population of the atoll comes from castaways from canoes driven hundreds of miles off their courses. They're

mainly Polynesians there—different from your people here—
with straight hair, light brown skin and quite big."

We had a drink and Darcy got out of his chair. "I must turn
you off now; I want to go to bed," he said. "Burns Philp's ship
is leaving on Wednesday; see me when you come back."

I thanked him and climbed the hill to my house. Next
morning when I looked down from the verandah at daylight,
the *Wai-ai* was back at her berth and the *Tulagi* had gone.

The fierce golden sun filled the cloudless blue sky and
drenched the ship in glaring light. A school of porpoises had
gambolled round the ship for hours but now lay astern, and
the glassy sea was disturbed only by the quick movements of
flying fish. High above, sea birds, with barely a flicker of
wing, glided idly in air currents, keeping up with us as though
in escort. It was a period of heat and calm in the north-west
monsoon season, a time when islanders make long voyages by
canoe.

The *Mahaga* made the voyage from Tulagi to Ong Tong
Java two or three times a year with stores for the trader and to
load the copra bought from the natives. She was not much more
than three hundred tons; she was old, dirty and small; she was
infested with bugs, and there was no escape in her from the
stink of copra. I had come aboard that afternoon in Tulagi, but
had seen only Belshaw the captain. He now came down from
the bridge, fat but strong and active, his fleshy red face con-
trasting with his prematurely white hair. He joined me at the
rail and then at his suggestion I followed him into the saloon
for tea. Cups and a large enamel tea-pot with sugar and a tin
of milk stood on the cigarette-scarred table. Perry, the engineer,
bald headed, sparely built and tall, came in after us and greeted
me affably. Tom Sleigh, super-cargo in the *Mahaga* to learn
the island trade, followed him and made a facetious remark
about cribbage. The mate came last. I had never seen him
before, and Belshaw introduced him awkwardly as 'Mr Price'.
He was below average height and slimly built, but his straight
back and thin-lipped mouth gave him a certain distinction. He

had a swarthy cadaverous face and when he spoke a trace of
accent told me he was a Welshman. There was an air of
constraint when he joined us at the table and I tried to make
conversation.

"I didn't know Robbie had left the ship," I said.

Belshaw put down his cup.

"Robbie? Poor Robbie's not too good," he said. "He's in
hospital in Sydney."

Perry ended the sympathetic silence which followed.

"It's his kidneys, isn't it?" he asked.

"Yeh, it's his kidneys," Belshaw said.

"Did you know Robbie?" I asked Price.

He shook his head. "No," he said. "I never met him."

Perry and Sleigh went to the store on the poop to play
cribbage. Belshaw and I sat on smoking, but Price refused a
cigarette.

"How long have you been in the Islands?" I asked him.

He looked at me disconcertingly as though resenting my
enquiry. "A bit over a year," he said. "I came down to recruit
with Larsen, but he went out to Ong Tong Java and I was on
the beach. I joined this ship a couple of months ago after
Robinson was sent down to Sydney."

"We'll be seeing Lafe Larsen at Ong Tong Java," Belshaw
added, as though imparting news of special interest. "With
the price of copra going the way it is, it would have been better
for him if he had stuck to recruiting."

Price took some magazines from a pile on a locker and went
out.

"You have got something new in mates," I said to Belshaw.

"Too right I have," he growled moodily.

"What's the matter with him?"

"What's the matter with him? He never has a drink, he
doesn't smoke and he has nothing to say except when he grouses
about the tucker. He gets on my nerves."

Belshaw pulled himself to his feet to go out. "I will say this
for him, though," he added, "he knows his work and the crew
will do anything for him."

My room was on the port side next to the mate's and to the bathroom. I bathed and changed early and stood out at the rail. The sun was beginning to turn a fiery red and to sink out of sight. Price, in dressing-gown and slippers, came out.

"Isn't that a glorious sunset," he said and, then shuffled off towards the bathroom.

At dinner Price exasperated me by refusing most of the food. During fitful conversation over coffee I asked Belshaw the probable time of our arrival.

"It's twenty-four hours from Tulagi," he said. "If we are on our course you may see coconuts at about three o'clock tomorrow and we should be in the anchorage between four and five." He got up and left, and Perry and Sleigh began to play cribbage. Price went soon after, and I followed. The piston thrust of the old engine sent a pulsating rhythm through the ship. In spite of the heat and of the discomfort of my bunk I was soon asleep.

The next day was again hot; the sun beat down, heating exposed iron-work until it was too hot to touch. Someone hooked a young kingfish during the morning and there were fried fish cutlets and potatoes for lunch. Price refused the food, and when the boy went back to the galley I heard the voice of the Chinese cook raised in sibilant protest.

A little before three o'clock I was roused by a shout from the look-out; half an hour later, with Belshaw's glasses, I saw clusters of coconut palms straight ahead in a silver and azure haze, and then the first of the islands ranged round an irregular-shaped reef. The coral islands lie so low that they are sometimes hard to find. At an early tea Belshaw boasted jocularly of his navigation.

We steamed slowly through a narrow passage close to two of the islands and then across the limpid water of the lagoon to an anchorage in front of nondescript buildings on Leuen-euwa, the big island where most of the people lived. A schooner was tied up at a pier of broken coral limestone.

Three natives in an outrigger canoe put off from the beach; two of them paddled and the third sat holding something on his knees. When they drew near to the ship I saw the two men were middle-aged and the other man much older. They clambered clumsily on to the gangway, climbed slowly up and then moved off in file round the ship speaking to no one. The first man strewed the ship with coconut fronds, the second scattered ashes and sprinkled water from a coconut water-pot, the old man came last muttering an invocation. They went all over the ship, then without a word to anyone they stepped cautiously down the gangway to their canoe and paddled back to the beach.

"Who are those people?" I asked Mareo.

"We call them *makua*," he said. "They come to drive devils away from the ship so that no evil is taken ashore when strangers come."

While he spoke I saw a second canoe had put off; in it was a white man whom I took to be Larsen. He stood up when the canoe was alongside and then almost ran up the gangway.

"It's time you came," he shouted. "I've had no grog for a month."

When he stepped on to the deck-plates I saw that grey hair sprouted in bristles from his closely cropped skull and that his shining freshly shaven face was bleeding from a small cut. His mouth hung open, wet lipped and loose, and his eyes were excited and hot. The clean khaki-drill trousers and the vest he was wearing were creased as though they had just been taken out of a box. He was barefooted.

"Tommy," he bawled at Sleigh, "open up your store and give me six bottles of White Horse and a pound of Ruby tobacco."

Larsen talked excitedly as Belshaw led him to the saloon. He gulped the whisky poured out for him and pushed the glass forward for more.

"Wait a minute, Lafe," Belshaw said earnestly. "Tommy wants to talk about your shipment."

Sleigh, young and assertive, cigarette in mouth, tapped the table with a pencil.

"It's like this, Lafe," he said. "Burns Philp have got one of

144

Waterside homes on stilts

Beating bark cloth

A meeting with elders

Schooner anchorage, Tulagi

Weir's ships on charter and they want to make a big shipment direct to the U.K. We are scraping up all the copra we can get. They are giving you £15 a ton here on the beach for this shipment. If we miss it you get the ordinary price less charges, and that won't be £15 per ton, I can tell you."

Larsen was speechless for a moment. He looked shocked, but quickly recovered himself and stood up.

"What are you talking about? £15 per ton!" he exclaimed angrily. "I want £25 a ton. I didn't come out here for my health."

Belshaw intervened. "It's no good arguing with Tommy," he said. "He's telling you what B.P.'s told him to tell you. You're a bit out of touch here, Lafe," he went on. "The price has been falling for weeks. You're lucky to get £15; you won't get that again for a long time."

Larsen had regained his composure. £15 a ton probably gave him a good profit, I thought.

"With the big dances going on now, I can't get any boys to carry my copra; I'll want your deck-hands," he said.

"That's O.K.," Belshaw replied. "How much you got?"

"I've got a hundred ton here and forty to be brought in and bagged."

"Forget about the stuff to be brought in; we'll get that next time. This is a hurry-up job. We sail at noon tomorrow, and that's leaving it close to discharge and load into the charter ship by five o'clock the day after."

"Not on your life: you load everything," Larsen declared. "I want the best price for all I've got. You leave here by two tomorrow and you'll be in Tulagi by two the day after—if you push her, you'll be in before that."

Belshaw's face turned a deeper red and he looked nettled.

"If we leave later than noon tomorrow, I can't guarantee your copra will get you £15 a ton. I don't want you belly-aching at me if we don't get there in time." He spoke loudly but Larsen was unmoved. "That's all right," he said confidently. "I'll send out for that copra now."

Price came into the room and Larsen greeted him effusively

but I did not see what passed between them as the native bo'sun announced that a boat was in the water for me.

There was barely a ripple on the surface of the lagoon as two native sailors with an oar apiece pulled effortlessly and without haste towards the white coral beach. They steered dextrously between coral heads where tiny multi-coloured fish swimming in orderly formation crossed each other's tracks before they disappeared into the obscure recesses of the coral. Then suddenly there was a violent commotion and small fish in a shoal darted repeatedly out of the water as though leap-frogging across the lagoon. Frigate birds, attracted by the commotion, wheeled overhead and occasionally swooped down and flew off with a fish. A kingfish, over-reaching itself in pursuit, shot explosively ten feet up into the air, then, with a convulsive twist, turned and plunged downward and re-entered the water in a silver flash. In an instant it was over and again the waters of the lagoon lay tranquil, shimmering, unruffled in the sun.

It was low tide, and when the boat grounded naked children, glancing at me shyly as they came wading out, helped the sailors to drag the boat up the beach. A well-trodden path came out from the closely growing coconut palms and ran along the top of the beach to Larsen's place away to our right. The house and outbuildings looked dilapidated and in need of paint. Scraggy fowls scratching in the coral sand and a long-legged sow with a litter of young added to the impression of desolation. We took the path to the centre of the island where the coconut palms grew so closely—some towering up success-fully towards the light and some crowded out, sickly and twisted between them—that we seemed to be walking between walls. Mareo spoke to two youths who had watched our arrival and they went ahead to give warning of our coming.

Shouts came from Larsen's place as we strode on. His schooner was already on her way down the lagoon and as the sound of her engine grew fainter, I heard the ship's launch engine start up.

New sounds reached us as we went forward—chanting and

rhythmic hand-clapping came from somewhere ahead. The sounds grew louder as we went on, but the performers were still some way off when the path widened at a clearing in the grove. Large slabs of lime-washed coral stood ranged in rows. It was a burial place, Mareo told me, and there were people at work there with besoms sweeping away leaves and brushing out marks on the sandy expanse of the clearing. There was patience and resignation in their manner. I stopped walking and watched them.

"They are wife, husband, son or daughter of someone buried here," Mareo remarked.

"Mourners?"

"Yes."

"How long do they go on doing this?"

"For half the day."

"Yes, but for how many weeks?"

"They stay there for one year or more."

"For a year?"

"Yes, there is a house for men and for women; they live here, but sometimes they sleep on the graves. Their people bring them food."

I stared a little longer and then we walked on towards the village. The sound of the chanting and hand-clapping grew louder as we went forward. When we came upon the village there was a lull and people stood in groups in an open space in the middle of the village as though waiting for something to happen. Large piles of coconut husks and the smell of fish told of feasting. The chief sat in a large heavy chair designed like a throne. He sat before his palm-thatch hut surrounded by his councillors. I greeted him and gave him the case of plug tobacco I had brought him from Darcy. He spoke of the affairs of the atoll and I noted his requests as Mareo interpreted. Then, as though he had wearied of talk, he made a signal and his attendants moved sedately to the open ground. They were imposing men, tall, straight-haired, and light coffee-coloured. Some broke into a chant and the others, unsmiling, started to dance with leisurely measured steps. Men in the crowd joined in with a leap and the dance went on to its abrupt conclusion.

The dances and the intervals between them went on for more than an hour. The noise, the reeking smell of fish and the confinement of the closely growing coconuts were becoming more than I could bear. I told Mareo to tell the chief it was time for me to go, but now everyone was looking away and there were shouts of acclamation. Then I saw the girls of the place, coloured yellow with aromatic turmeric and adorned with flowers and feathers. Quite naked, they gravely walked hand in hand, two by two, along the village street. They went to the end of the village, wheeled round past the huts and slowly returned as the crowd opened to make way for them. There were cries from young men as the girls went by, but nothing obscured the dignity of this unexpected parade; there was nothing indecent about these solemn maidens.

"What's it about?" I asked Mareo.

"It is the end of the dancing," he said.

"Why are the girls walking about like this?"

"The unmarried girls always do this after the dancing—in three or four days plenty will be married."

I bade the chief farewell and followed Mareo along the narrow path back to the beach in search of a boat to go off to the *Mahaga*. The sun had set and I stumbled awkwardly over coconuts on the path and brushed against twisted palms as we retraced our steps in the darkness. A dim light came from a hut near the burial grounds and shadowy figures moved about among the graves. Then I heard shouts of laughter and soon we reached the beach and found Sleigh with his wide-brimmed hat on the back of his head, a cigarette in his mouth, seated on a box and by the light of hurricane lamps weighing bags of copra brought from the sheds near Larsen's house. Labourers took up the heavy bags from the weighing machine and carried them down the beach at a trot and then, wading out knee deep through the water, dropped them off into a boat. The winches of the *Mahaga* were at work on the previous load; Sleigh said it would be fifteen minutes before the next load left. I told Mareo he could go back to the village and I walked over to the house to wait. I saw Belshaw, Perry and Larsen in the light on the verandah. Belshaw gave me a boisterous greeting when he saw me. "Come and have a drink," he boomed and, turning to Larsen, he declared: "He's a good scout."

"Too right he's a good scout," said Larsen, getting up. "Come and sit down."

"Did you enjoy the dancing?" Belshaw asked.

There would be tiresome ribaldry if I told them about the girls, I thought, so I said nothing.

"How's the loading going?" I asked.

"It's going good," Belshaw said. "We'd be away by eleven o'clock tomorrow if we just took the stuff in the shed, but this stupid bastard wants us to wait until two o'clock to put in another forty-odd tons. I tell him we'll miss that shipment from Tulagi."

Larsen looked at him with exasperation, but he spoke without offence.

"You make me tired," he said. "You say we got to be there by half-past two, and it takes twenty-four hours for the trip."

"Have it your own way, Lafe boy," Belshaw said as he moodily reached for the bottle, "but don't blame me if anything goes wrong; that's all I ask."

Sleigh came up the verandah steps into the light and told me the launch was waiting. I thanked Larsen for the drink and got up to go. Perry also stood up. He put a hand on Sleigh's shoulder. "Sit down, Tommy," he said, "let me give you a spell." Sleigh took Perry's chair. "Got a bottle of beer for me, Lafe?" I heard him ask as I walked with Perry towards the beach.

I was carried through the water to the boat and climbed over the copra bags to the launch. The launch towed the loaded boat and moved slowly out to the *Mahaga* as she lay at anchor with her lights ablaze and looking bigger than by day.

Price was standing at the top of the gangway when I got aboard. He was embarrassed when he saw me.

"I thought you were sleeping ashore with the others," he said.

"Not a chance," I replied, and went to my cabin.

I bathed and changed quickly and went straight to the saloon. The boy looked at me doubtfully as he served the food. We had thin soup, steamed fish and a milk pudding. When the table was cleared, I sat drinking coffee.

"Pretty dull meal," I said for the want of something to say.

"It's my fault; I ordered it," Price admitted. "I can't stand the greasy food Belshaw likes."

"Do you have stomach trouble?"

"I've an ulcer which flares up at times."

I looked at him with astonishment.

"Why don't you tell Belshaw and get a suitable diet?"

Price had shed some of his reserve; he seemed glad to talk.

"If I told him, B.P.'s would find out and I'd lose this job. I might go sick at any time."

"It's your business," I said after brief reflection, "but I think you're wrong."

We said no more about it. The saloon was airless and close and we went out on deck. Bursts of laughter carried clearly across the lagoon from Larsen's house. Lights flickered ashore and occasionally canoes moved silently in the gloom between the ship and the beach. I had nothing to say. Price broke the silence.

"Do you like the islands?" he asked.

His question took me aback.

"Yes," I said shortly. "I'm interested in my work; there's nothing else I want to do."

"You're lucky."

I sought no confidences from Price, but I found myself beginning to pity the man.

"If you don't like it, why do you stay here?" I asked.

"I must have a job; I've a wife and three children in Sydney." He paused as though undecided whether to say more, and then went on. "When I came down here for Larsen, I'd been without work for six months. I've got an extra-master's ticket; I was in one of the Braemar ships, but I had a row and threw my hand in. I couldn't get a job with any of the other coastal companies. I was getting desperate when I met Larsen."

"Larsen's schooner must have been a change after the smart Braemar ships," I said.

"It was hellish, and I didn't trust Larsen."

"What's the matter with Larsen?"

"He's a crook; he swindled me."

I knew Larsen to be a feckless improvident trader and recruiter, but I had heard nothing worse about him.

"How did he swindle you?" I asked.

"He promised me twenty pounds a month plus two pounds a head for every recruit I got."

"What did you know about labour recruiting?"

"Nothing, but I learned," Price replied bitterly. "In the four months I was with him I made three trips to Malaita and one to Santa Cruz. I got him over a hundred recruits and then I went into Tulagi Hospital with malaria and stomach trouble. He sent my kit round there and an order on Burns Philp for twenty pounds. Then he came out here and left me on the beach."

"Have you asked him for money?"

"How could I? I haven't seen him until today. But it would be a waste of time anyway."

"You might get some of your money if you asked him."

"He knew I was hard up. He'll never pay me. He's a drunken little bastard. I'd kick his teeth in if I had half a chance."

I made no reply and Price soon got over his violent outburst. "Forget it," he said in calmer tones. "I'm talking too much." He looked at his watch. "The boy puts out cocoa for me now; would you like some?"

"No, thank you," I said. "I'm going to bed."

I read the scrawled note Price handed me at breakfast and confirmed his reading. I told him why Belshaw had changed the time of departure to two o'clock. His muttered reply was inaudible. We finished breakfast in silence and he went ashore.

I sat in a deck-chair on the bridge and read all the morning. At one o'clock the launch went back to the beach without an empty boat in tow and I came down to the deck to watch the last load from the shore. The boat was less than half full and labourers sat in silence on the bags. Five white men were in the launch. Belshaw slowly climbed the gangway, Larsen followed helped by Perry, then came Sleigh and last of all, Price. The launch boy and another native carried up a wooden chest and a suit-case. Price passed me on his way to his room; the other four went into the saloon. Larsen was unshaven and dirty and looked as though he had slept in his clothes, but he was very cheerful. Belshaw called for beer. Price joined us but he refused a drink. He went out again when the native bo'sun peered round the door to say that the boats and launch had been hoisted aboard.

The anchor came up just after two o'clock and the telegraph sounded from the bridge. The *Mahaga* went ahead slowly across the lagoon, through the passage between the islands, and then out to sea.

I had drunk more beer than I was used to and after lunch I fell into a deep sleep. It was late when I woke up and came out on deck. The others had finished tea and were sitting in the saloon. Larsen was drinking. He was an incongruous figure as he poured out whisky for himself and chanted snatches of song in a thick slurred voice.

"Give him a woodener, someone," Belshaw suggested.

Sleigh took the bottle and poured out half a glass of whisky.

"Come on, Lafe, bottoms up!" he urged.

Larsen gulped the whisky and Sleigh immediately poured out more. Soon after the second drink Larsen slumped in his chair and began to snore.

"There's a camp-bed for him on the bridge," Belshaw said.

Perry and Sleigh, taking him by the shoulders and feet, carried him up the companionway.

No one talked at dinner. Sleigh was grey with fatigue and went off as soon as we had finished, without waiting for coffee. Perry nodded when Belshaw asked if he could increase speed. Belshaw then spoke to Price and bade us good-night. Perry and Price went to their cabins, but I was restless after my after-noon sleep and the night was hot. I sat alone in the saloon and looked at the old magazines before I went to bed. After an uneasy half-sleep I sat up, the sheets and pillow were saturated with sweat and I felt stifled. Cockroaches scurried under my feet when I switched on the naked light and got down from the bunk. I switched off the light and stood in the darkness outside. The pulsating throb of the engine and the overtones of creaks and rattles were greater than before; vibration set my tooth-brush and razor rattling in the washstand. Phosphor-escent froth raced by from the bow wave as the thrust of the propeller drove the old ship on at unaccustomed speed. I heard the metallic clang of a furnace door. A native fireman appeared silently in the darkness hoisting ash up the ventilator shaft; he emptied the bucket over the side and returned to the engine room without seeing me. I moved to the side of the ventilator and pressed back against the bulkhead; it was clammy with moisture condensed from the warm humid air. Then Price appeared in a flood of light from the mate's cabin and moved swiftly up the companionway to the bridge. I waited for him to return, but I was overcome with drowsiness and returned to my bunk without seeing him.

I was the first in the saloon next morning and had started breakfast when Perry joined me. Sleigh followed a few minutes later. He greeted us both and added: "We haven't made good time; we should have passed Cape Prieto long ago." Perry nodded and said: "Yeh."

Belshaw, Price and Larsen were talking together as they came in.

"I don't understand," Belshaw said.

"I can't help it, I'm afraid. I turned in early last night and slept until daylight," Price replied.

Belshaw said nothing, and Price added as he opened his table napkin: "I've heard that currents among these islands are very irregular and of course you get strong tidal sets."

Belshaw looked worried. "I've seen nothing like it before," he said. "It must have been a strong set or a current."

Larsen gazed from one man to another, hanging on their words.

"We'll make Tulagi by three o'clock?" he asked anxiously.

"I hope so, I hope so," Belshaw replied stonily, and started his breakfast.

Perry went to the engine room and Sleigh to the store on the poop. Belshaw and Price went up to the bridge. The boy cleared the table and I sat on the settee and picked up the old magazines. Larsen sat facing me. He had eaten nothing at breakfast, but had asked for more coffee. His left cheek twitched repeatedly and he raised the cup to his mouth with both hands. He lamented that through his folly he had lost a good price for his copra. His reiterations became wearisome, and when I told him it was too soon to say, he relapsed into a brooding silence. I left him and walked along the deck, then picked my way between groups of deck hands on the hatch and went up to the store on the poop. Sleigh had made the place comfortable with easy chairs. He and Perry were playing cribbage. "Is that all you two ever do?" I asked. Neither of them spoke or looked up, and I felt rebuffed. I went forward again and climbed up to the bridge. Price was on watch. He glanced at me but said nothing. Belshaw was in his room. I descended the companion-way and stood under the scrap of awning outside my room as we steamed by Buena Vista and Olevuga Island towards Gela. Half an hour later Larsen joined me.

"Seen that?" he asked looking astern.

"What?" I said following his gaze.

"There's something coming up from the nor'west."

I looked again and saw a small black cloud just above the horizon.

"We'll be in Tulagi before that comes to anything," I said. But as I spoke there was a gust of wind.

"Don't you believe it," Larsen said.

There were more gusts and they were stronger; a long heavy swell followed the ship.

"We'll have a blow," Larsen said, turning away and going up to the bridge.

154

Dark clouds were rapidly filling the sky and it began to blow steadily from the nor'west. I watched the gathering storm—there was half a gale blowing and the sea was confused —but the violence of the storm was short lived; the wind dropped suddenly and then rain fell. It fell vertically, relentlessly and with unvarying intensity. It formed a barrage of water obscuring everything more than thirty yards ahead. Belshaw had reduced speed and the ship was barely under way. I sat in the saloon thumbing the old magazines to occupy myself until lunch. Larsen came in and sat down at the table with his head in his hands. "Don't give up hope," I said, but he was too dispirited to reply.

Larsen and I were the only two in for lunch, and as soon as it was over I left him and went to my room. Water came in round a rivet and leaked in slow-forming drops on to the bunk. I put a towel to catch the water and lay down. The clatter of things in the washstand roused me from sleep. The ship was now going ahead at full speed; the rain had stopped and the sun was shining from a clear sky.

Larsen was talking disconnectedly to Sleigh in the saloon. His mood alternated between despair and lively optimism.

We had now come up to the islands southward from Tulagi Harbour. I went out on deck and Price came down from the bridge.

"What time will we get in?" I asked.

"The old man thinks it'll be between half-past five and six." He broke off and gazed fixedly towards the two islands ahead.

"There she is," he said. "See her?—look, between the islands."

Larsen and Sleigh were now standing with us at the rail.

"Are you sure it's her?" Sleigh asked him.

"Oh yes, I can see her quite plainly; she's a Weir ship all right—don't often see Andrew Weir's ships in this part of the world." He left us and went to his room.

Larsen sought relief from disappointment in a stream of obscenity. "Easy, Lafe, easy," Sleigh remonstrated. "You are no worse off than you would have been without this chance."

"That's the point: I had a chance to square B.P.'s and get out of that place. Now I'll have to go back. You don't know what it's like there on your own." His voice became a whimper and I thought he would break down. Sleigh looked at him with silent compassion. "Hard cheese, Lafe boy, hard cheese," he said after a moment. "Come up to the poop and I'll give you a drink."

We tied up at Burns Philp's Makambo Wharf at a quarter to six and I left the ship. A young clerk hurrying from one of the company's offices asked me if Larsen was on board. Mareo carried my suit-case to a launch that was waiting for me at the wharf steps. I spent the night at the Residency.

"You look better than you did when I saw you at Tataba; was the trip interesting?" Darcy said when he came back from the Club.

"Very interesting," I said, but he barely listened to what I told him about Ong Tong Java.

"I believe in leaving people in remote places to themselves unless we can really help," Darcy said. "Their own organisations work pretty well. Traders respect their tabus and customs to get goodwill for trade."

"Yes, I suppose so," I agreed.

The flame tree I had seen when I had first arrived at Tulagi was in full bloom. It was still light enough to see it from the Residency verandah.

"Isn't that tree lovely?" Darcy asked abruptly.

The boy was setting up the big brass tray with glasses and decanters. There was nothing more to be said about Ong Tong Java.

"Yes, it's gorgeous," I said.

For fifteen minutes I did nothing, then I peered below. Sweat poured down Soge's back as he worked with heavy spanners. Gagi squatted at his side, looking on with concern.

"Engine start soon?" I asked.

Soge turned his strained face towards me.

"I don't know, sir," he replied.

"You know what's wrong?"

"Not yet."

For four hours the *Wai-ai*, thrust along by her engine, had made good time across a shimmering hazy sea. When we passed Buena Vista at one o'clock I thought I might be in time to see the storekeeper that afternoon. Half an hour later, as I finished lunch, the engine spluttered and became silent.

It was the end of the March quarter and I had decided on an impulse to visit Tulagi when the *Wai-ai* went in for station supplies. With the ship drifting helplessly two hours after her engine had stopped, I cursed the impulse and went to my bunk in the hope of relieving the tedium by going to sleep.

At a quarter-past four the engine came to life with a strong healthy beat. The fuel oil was dirty and Soge had cleaned out the tank.

The Bungana beacon light was burning when we reached the islands off Tulagi. I looked forward to an early night and a busy day to follow. Wesu trimmed and lighted the side lights and we made a wide sweep round the islands on a course straight down the fairway into the harbour. At twenty minutes past seven we tied up at Government Wharf and I changed and stepped ashore. A heavy brass lamp, locked to the top of a post, gave light to the wharf, but beyond it was dark. I made my way with a torch past weatherboard buildings—post office, treasury and labour office—and then thirty yards farther on I left the waterside path and climbed the coral gravel path to the hotel which stood forty or fifty feet up on the hillside.

There were tales of fabulous spending at Elkington's Hotel. Traders and recruiters off schooners used to come ashore in the 'twenties and buy up the entire stock of liquor. The copra slump had brought an end to spectacular extravagance but not to hard drinking. As he grew older, Tom Elkington cultivated an air of rectitude, and those who wanted to go beyond the limits he allowed in his hotel—eccentrics, beachcombers and drunkards—found what they wanted at Sterling's Hotel on the waterfront in Chinatown.

The radiance of the bar lamps pierced the gloom outside and touched the frangipani trees and the hibiscus bushes along the path. The sickly fragrance of orange blossom hung in the still air. In the lush vegetation behind the hotel cicadas chirruped without ceasing, and fireflies flickered in spasmodic flight. It was a fine night. The Southern Cross gleamed unmistakably in the cloudless starlit sky. It was warm and I was sweating when I reached the hotel verandah, but I had forgotten the frustration of the afternoon and felt composed. The best hours in the tropics are early night when darkness subdues the harsh excess of colour and light and often there is quiet.

I looked into the bar on my way to the dining-room. Two people were there talking to Tom. The white hair and bulky figure of Belshaw were unmistakable. The moment I looked his way he turned his head and our eyes met. He hailed me at once and I joined them. His companion, a beady eyed, sallow man with incipient dewlaps, was Robinson. After the flurry of greetings I asked Robinson about his health and then accepted a drink from Belshaw.

"I haven't seen you for months," Belshaw said, "not since you did that trip with us to Ong Tong Java."

"No," I replied. "I don't come in here more often than I can help."

As the first surprise of our meeting subsided, I found little to say. Robinson ordered drinks.

"Any news of Lafe Larsen?" I asked.

"Lafe? Lafe's on the pig's back; he's doing fine. He was here last night."

"What do you mean? I thought he'd gone back to Ong Tong Java?"

Belshaw put his glass down noisily.

"Didn't you hear about Lafe?" he demanded with surprise.

I laughed. "I never hear anything at Tataba."

"I thought everyone knew about Lafe. When we tied up

158

that day B.P.'s manager sent for him. He could hardly speak when he came back. An hour after that Weir ship sailed, the Sydney office radioed they could pay £19 a ton. By being late Lafe made the best part of another thousand pounds. A week later the price fell again. Lafe's in the clear now."

I shook my head with bewilderment. The island trade baffled me.

"What an extraordinary stroke of luck for Larsen," I said.

"Yes, he was lucky all right. I thought he'd gone mad when he came back and told me. Then there was the trouble with that mate we had—Price. D'you remember him?"

"Certainly I remember him," I said. "He was a strange chap."

"My oath! he was strange. Would you believe it, Lafe wanted to pay him some money he owed him from some old recruiting business, but Price turned round and hit him."

"Hit him, what for?"

"Search me; then he apologised and started getting Lafe a drink."

"Well!" I exclaimed, "what a to-do."

"Price refused to take the money and then a couple of days later he went sick with stomach trouble and the doc sent him down to Sydney."

"Poor chap," I said. "I'm sorry."

"Oh, he's all right again, Robbie saw him in Sydney."

"Yes," Robinson said. "I met him in B.P.'s office about three months ago. He looked fine. He's got a good job ashore with one of the oil companies. They think a lot of him."

Belshaw finished his drink and put his glass down. He shook his head sagaciously. "May be so, but he's a funny bastard all right, that Price. He didn't fit in down here."

I agreed with him. "The same again please Tom," I said.

I signed the chit. "Let's sit on the verandah," I suggested. "It's nice out there."

CHAPTER SEVEN

Another Part of the Island

IT was not a big island and much of it was mangrove swamp, but there were clumps of high trees, and perched in the branches of these trees there were pigeons beyond number. The deafening uproar of their cooing went on without pause. I stood on the strip of sandy silt above high water and took aim. Two pigeons fell when I fired and the cooing suddenly stopped; but in five seconds, long before Hiro had picked up the two birds, it had begun again, as loud as ever.

A mile beyond the island we took a south-west course through the barrier reef for Edu. The sound of the pigeons grew fainter as we steered round Wreck Point at the northern extreme of Ysabel and kept our course against the tidal flow between the mainland and the islands to the north. We anchored in front of the village.

Edu people were unlike other people of Ysabel; they spoke a different language and their customs and beliefs were different. They had been headhunters; there were many of them alive who had taken part in raids. There was widespread belief that they had joined forces with raiders from other islands slaughtering men, women and children along the coast of Ysabel and carrying off grisly trophies to be stripped of tissue for the adornment of *tabu*-houses. The story of the old treachery persisted and provided substance for the distant manner with which Edu people were treated by other natives of Ysabel. But they had become staunch adherents of the mission and while we lay at anchor the sound of toneless hymn singing came from the shore and reminded me that it was Sunday.

Huts, well built of sago-palm leaf and split bamboo, stood on piles in shallow water along the shore; more huts were scattered over rising land in the foothills of a peak with a banyan at its summit. The young men of the place were often away diving for shell, fishing or on expeditions in search of turtles. They were a prosperous lively people, but something had gone wrong. This was my second visit to them in less than a month. I had come away last time disturbed by the apathy of the men. They had not been so alert or healthy looking as they had previously appeared and the village had been dirty. Bako, the headman, had been evasive, but had assured me that all would be well on my next visit.

A canoe put off and came alongside and two men were helped aboard. One had the soft massive podginess of elephantiasis and the other was a sparely built man of medium height, darker coloured than his companion. He was Gole, Bako's assistant.

I greeted him. "Where's Bako?" I asked.

"He's sick in his hut; he tell me to meet you."

"I'm sorry; I'll come ashore and see him presently."

This news about Bako added to the abnormality and the stress I felt at my work.

"How is everything here?" I asked.

"There is bad news. A man named Rufa has killed his wife and two children."

I felt a quiver of trepidation, but I told myself I was not really surprised at what he said.

"How did he kill them?"

"With his axe."

"With an axe?"

"Yes, with a tomahawk kind of axe."

I knew what he meant—the long-handled small-headed axe brought by early traders. It was a weapon more deadly than the wooden club of the islands—it had very little use as a tool.

Gole spoke to the man with elephantiasis and the fat man knelt on the deck and reached down to the canoe. He brought up an axe. Gole pointed to a sticky brown discoloration on the shaft near the head and then held out the axe for me to see.

"This is Rufa's axe," he said.

Gole spoke again to the fat man, who handed him a match box. He opened it and showed me a fragrant of thin white bone and some furry hair, hair bleached white with lime, the hair of a child.

"We find these things in Rufa's canoe," he said.

He closed the box and handed it to Hiro. Hiro took it and the axe below to my cabin.

Gole remained where he was.

"Who saw the bodies?" I asked him.

"Nobody saw them."

He read doubt in my face.

"It's quite true, sir," he added. "Rufa killed his wife and two children. He must have thrown the bodies in the sea and a shark or alligator took them."

He spoke listlessly, and for a moment I wondered whether he was being impertinent; but he suddenly shook with a rigor.

"You are sick," I said.

"Yes, I have fever, but Bako wanted me to meet you."

"You ought to be on your bed."

He made no reply, and I turned to Hiro.

"Give him quinine, aspirin and Epsom Salts."

I spoke to the man again when he had taken the medicine.

"Go to your house and cover yourself with a blanket."

I ordered Hoile to go ashore with Gole to arrest the man Rufa and hold him until the morning. Later I went ashore with Hiro to see Bako. I walked up the beach to his hut. Earlier in the day my clothes had got wet, but now in the wind and warm sun they were beginning to dry on me.

We walked through the scattered collection of sago-palm thatch huts with fishing-nets stretched out to dry on bamboo posts, and passed a large canoe-house and a *tabu*-house containing monstrous cult objects. Blue smoke hung about in the still evening air as women prepared food, and their naked brown children played near by on the sandy ground, driving

163

off foraging pigs and fowls when they came too near. Wood smoke, fish and copra gave off a rank throat-catching stench varying in strength as we walked past the huts. I had never seen so many men at Edu, sitting idly chewing areca nuts or smoking trade pipes. A few women came out of the little church building as we passed.

Bako was up when we got to his hut. Someone must have warned him of our coming. His manner was correct, but there was no warmth in his greeting. He reminded me of Kepi, with his large expressive eyes and light-coloured skin, and he had the same well-knit figure. His hair was as short as a woman's; his tightly wrapped *lava lava* showed him to have narrow hips.

We spoke about the murder; then I enquired about the state of things at Edu. He appeared reluctant to talk. He may have been sick or he may have preferred to say nothing.

"There are a lot of men at home," I said.

"Yes, there are," he agreed.

"I have never seen so many before."

"No, nor have I."

I made little headway with him.

"I hope you'll soon be better," I said. "Is there any medicine you want?"

He shook his head wearily. I may not have heard him correctly when he spoke.

"There's nothing you can do," I thought he said. "No, there's nothing. I'll soon be better."

I left him and walked back through the village with Hiro. I felt I was being shut out from something.

"There's something wrong at this place," I said.

"Everybody's afraid of something," he replied.

"What's frightening them?"

"I don't know."

I held the magistrate's enquiry in the *Wai-ai*. I stood on the bit of deck amidships between the cabin and the engine room. There was no wind, and I put my papers on the cabin housing and wrote standing. The missing woman's name was Lamota;

the older of the children was a girl, about eight years old I reckoned, named Tina, and the other child was a boy of about five years old named Dola.

Hoile brought Rufa to the port side deck. His face had the leaden hue of a sick blackman. He looked back at me with sombre indifference when I spoke his name. He was not asked to answer when I read out the charge, but he turned immediately to Hiro.

"I killed the woman and two children," he said. He had the air of a man ready there and then for punishment.

When I had heard the witnesses I decided there was a case for Rufa to answer, and I addressed him in the usual formula. The wretched man's face worked with perplexity. I found the proceedings hateful. He cracked the knuckle joints of his right hand. "Who can give evidence for me?" he demanded. Then he raised his voice. "I killed the woman and the two children with that axe and threw their bodies in the sea. This woman was wicked, she was plotting against me with Lobo," he shouted, and then fell silent.

This sudden outburst disconcerted me. I was conscious of my heart beating.

"Who's Lobo?" I asked, when I had regained my composure. He made no reply.

"Anything more?" I demanded.

He shook his head. "That's all," he said.

I wrote down what he had said and then read it out to him. He put his mark on the paper. I told him he would be sent to Tulagi for trial. His look of perplexity deepened. I told Hiro to tell him I had not the power to finish the affair. Hoile took him away.

After tea I stood for'ard in the *Wai-ai* and gazed at the surrounding scene. Edu was at the extreme north-western end of the island, on the shore of a narrow channel that wound through small islands. On the mainland a wooded mountain rose above the village; on the other side of the channel a chain of islands stretched away for miles to the northward. There was a time when I found the view from the anchorage magnificent and satisfying, but now I found it sombre and forbidding. Across the water I could see the island where long ago two Roman Catholic missionaries had been murdered for their meagre possessions. Beyond the village, on a small sandy beach on the mainland, a trader, careless for a moment, had been struck down and his schooner had been rifled. Head-hunters had returned home along the winding water-ways bringing with them the filth and stink of human butchery. There were men in the village who could recall those days and I found myself thinking of the harsh discomforts and barbarism of the past as I stood in the bow of the ship and looked about me. I had become oppressed with a feeling of foreboding.

A canoe put off from the shore. The man with elephantiasis paddled; Bako sat on the middle thwart in front of him. Hiro took Bako's hand and with the help of Gagi pulled him aboard. He looked strained and ill, but he had a determined air.

His monosyllabic response to my enquiry about his health was indistinct. His manner suggested he had no time for civilities.

"You can go now," he told me. "There's nothing to keep you here any longer."

"I am not leaving yet," I replied.

"Why?" he expostulated. "You've finished the murder case. It's time for you to go."

"What's wrong at Edu?" I demanded. "Why do you want me to go? What's the matter with all your people?"

Bako made no reply at first, and a look of pain came into his eyes. When he spoke, his talk was disconnected and obscure.

"It's better for us if you would go," he ended weakly. "You can't help us."

He got down into the canoe and went back to the beach.

I became acutely anxious. I found I could not sleep when I went to my bunk that night. Towards the dawn I fell into an uneasy doze. Hiro came to me in the morning when I stepped up on deck to shave. His expression was one of shocked incredulity.

"What's the matter with you?" I asked.

166

"News has just come from the village that Gole died last night."

"Gole died?" I exclaimed stupidly. "What are you talking about. I saw him yesterday."

"All the same he died last night. Some people say he get *devil.*"

I went ashore after breakfast. Gagi and Wesu rowed the boat and Hiro came with me. Women looked at us in a terror-stricken way and turned their backs on me as we passed. There was an air of open hostility among some of the men, and as we walked through the village to Bako's hut someone shouted after us in an angry vengeful tone. Hiro gasped, and looked back to see who it was who had shouted.

"Did you hear what he shouted?" I asked.

"That was Gole's brother," he said. "He said it was your fault Gole died; if you had gone, it would not have happened."

"What does he mean?"

"I don't know what he means. The people are behaving very strangely."

Bako's hut stood on high land behind the village. Tall slender erect areca-nut palms grew just below it. The nuts had turned orange yellow and would soon be ripe. Hiro shouted when we came to the entrance to the hut, but there was no reply.

"There's someone there," I said. "I heard movements."

Hiro shouted again and then went in. When he came out he gave me a quick look of appraisal.

"Bako won't see you. As long as you stay here there will be trouble. He begs you to leave."

"Go in and tell him I shall not leave until I know what's wrong at Edu. When I came here a month ago I could see that something was wrong. This time I see that things are worse. The people are not happy; the young men are at home instead of being away fishing or diving for shell; the women look frightened and the place is dirty."

Raised voices came from the hut. Hiro was very grave when he came out again.

"Bako is very angry. He says the people know what is wrong and that you make it worse."

"Come away," I told him. "We'll go back to the ship. Maybe I'll think of something to do."

As we walked down the slope to the waterside I heard the sound of heart-broken weeping. We paused at the hut from which the sound came and Hiro spoke to a boy.

"Who's that?" I said.

"It's Gole's wife," Hiro replied shortly.

I said nothing, and we went on down to the boat.

That afternoon Beni came to me and complained that no one in the village would trade fish, fowls or eggs with him. Such a thing had never happened to me before, but I did not make much of it. "You'll have to open some tins then," I said, as though the lack of friendliness ashore was of no account.

After tea I walked for exercise along one of the contour paths on the hillside. The path linked groups of houses, sometimes dropping down to the waterside and then going up again to houses built on sloping land above. I walked for a mile. On my way back I passed a group of people standing idly near a half-hidden hut set back on a patch of uncleared land at the head of a small inlet from the sea. I was about to quicken my pace when an old man came out with his forearms wet with blood. In his left hand he clutched a crudely butchered pig's head, and the animal's intestines, which had partly escaped his grip, trailed behind him. In his right hand he held two stones. He walked slowly into the sea until the water reached his knees. He dropped the pig's head and intestines and then he took the larger of the two stones in his left hand and beat it with the other. The sound was bell-like and penetrating. After a moment he broke into a whining tremulous howl. I was moved by the strange performance and stood wondering what would happen next. There was a sharp exclamation of astonishment from one of the bystanders, and then in the clear limpid water I saw a big shark swimming rapidly from deep water up the inlet. When it had partly grounded before him, the old man picked up the intestines and the head and fed the shark. He kept the head until the end, finally letting it go after some slight hesitation. Then with a flick of its powerful tail and with a swirling of the shallow water the shark turned round and swam out to sea. The old man, without a glance at the spectators, returned slowly to the hut. I followed the path across the hill-side back to the centre of the village. I went down to the beach and shouted to Hiro. He looked at me curiously when he got out of the boat, and joined me.

"We are going to see Bako," I told him.

He looked very surprised, but made no comment. We climbed the path to Bako's house in silence. Stars had come out. Twilight would soon turn into darkness.

"Shall I tell Bako you want him?" Hiro asked.

"No, I'm going in," I said.

Hiro showed me the way. A stifling smell came from the room where Bako lay. When he saw me he got up awkwardly from his mat and came out. He looked strained and drawn. I told him he must listen to me, and then I described what I had seen.

"Do you know the hut?" I asked.

"Yes, I know the place. It is very *tabu*."

"Why haven't I been told about it?"

Bako's uneasiness was obvious as he searched for an answer to my question.

"The old man has not been there very long," he said.

Bako's furtive manner added to my perplexity.

"You could have told me yesterday or today or last month when I was here."

Bako suddenly looked defenceless. The hostility which he had shown towards me earlier in the day had gone.

"This old man is a *devil devil* man. His name is Lobo, and he is a very bad man."

"What do you mean?"

"He can make people die. My people are afraid of him. He has said that you must not come to this place any more or more people will die. The people think Gole died because you would not go."

"Are you afraid of him?"

Bako spoke evasively. "Everyone is afraid of him. This man makes sacrifice with pigs and calls the shark and then somebody dies. Maybe somebody will die tonight."

I was very uneasy as I looked at Bako's trim figure and intelligent face.

"Do you really believe this?" I demanded.

Bako did not reply at once, and I reflected that in spite of years as a headman and in spite of great personal courage and intelligence he still clung to the crude superstitions of his people. He seemed to read my thoughts, when he replied, for his tone was aggressive.

"Lobo sacrificed pigs and called the shark two or three times before Gole died. I think someone else will soon die."

"Nonsense, Bako," I said. "Don't talk nonsense."

There was not much else I could say. Bako regarded me stolidly. "No, sir," was all he replied.

It was dark as we walked down the slope past the huts to the beach. I had treated Bako's fears with contempt, but Gole's death and the events of the evening had upset me. I delayed going to my bunk until midnight, and then I slept badly.

After breakfast I called Hiro.

"We must see this man Lobo," I said.

He licked his lips and looked about uneasily.

"Belema's sick," he replied.

Belema was the fat podgy man who attended on Bako and Gole.

"What's the matter with him?"

Hiro turned. He called to a youth sitting aft and eating rice with the crew. I knew him by sight, he was a light-hearted youth, a member of Bako's family. The boy got up, hitched his *lava lava* round his waist, and came along the deck to me. He was very grave.

"Bako send me to say Belema sick. About first fowl cry, he shout and struggle and fight like a crazy man. His wife come to Bako; Bako send people to hold Belema. By daylight time he quiet. He is very sick ready to die."

I dismissed the boy and he slipped overboard into his one-man canoe and paddled to the beach.

"We must see this man Lobo," I said again to Hiro.

"It would be better if we left this place now."

"Why?" I demanded sharply. "Are you scared too?"

Hiro had withdrawn into that state of distant reserve which I had noticed at the time of my trouble with Kile. But there was also embarrassment and shame in his manner.

"Scared! I'm not scared; but everyone says Lobo will make more people die if they talk to you."

"That will do," I said. "You take Wetera ashore and find out what you can about what's going on here."

He left me. I was horribly undecided and found I could neither read nor think. I had a meal at midday and tried to rest during the afternoon. Hiro and Wetera returned to the ship at four o'clock. I had tea and called Hiro to me. I asked him what he had discovered.

"Lobo is a *devil devil* man," he reported. "He started to call the shark about three months ago. He makes orders to people, and if they disobey they become sick and die. He has told the Edu people that they must not pay tax again or hear the word of Government. He says you must go, or more people will die. Everyone in Edu is afraid. Everyone fears that people are plotting with Lobo. Some people like Rufa are going mad. Rufa thought his wife was talking to Lobo about him. I think it better that we leave this place."

I thanked him and he went aft. I had become sensitive to change in the ship. Crew and police had almost imperceptibly allied themselves with the Edu people against me. There had been shouts of excitement when I had shot pigeons on the island at the beginning of the channel to Edu. The day before we had found anchorage to the west of a small island and I had stripped and dived in and had swum about lazily in the water inside the reef. Hiro and Wetera and two of the crew had joined me and there had been a lot of laughter when Beni had jumped in after them. I had lain for half an hour on the powdery sand of the beach. I had been relaxed and unusually content when I had come back to the ship. Later as stars had appeared and the moon had come up I had still been happy. Low-pitched untroubled voices of police and crew had reached me as they had lingered over their evening rice. I had felt a bond with these Solomon Islanders. In the morning I had joined them as they had delved for megapode eggs on the island. Now I felt no bond; I was among strangers. I was restless and miserable and at my wits' end. I could expect no help from anyone. I decided to go alone in search of Lobo.

The physical exertion of walking brought some relief. I passed five houses before I reached the descent to the *tabu*-house. One of them would be Lobo's. I found him in the third house that I peered into. He came out and fixed unwavering watchful eyes on me. His face was clean of stubble; hairs had been plucked out with great care. He had not the pendulous ear loops of the other old men of the place, but there were large discoloured patches on his skin which might have been the beginning of leprosy. He kept his uneasy close-set eyes on me. I was aware of two or three people behind me.

"Are you Lobo?" I asked in the Bugotu language of Ysabel.

"Yes, I am Lobo."

"I have been told that you have caused deaths of people in Edu."

There was a slight change in his expression. He looked back at me contemptuously.

"Yes, that is so. People have died. Belema will die next, then Bako, and then you."

A woman passed before him into the house. Lobo resented the interruption and addressed her furiously. It was the first show of feelings he had displayed. The woman cowered and edged her way fearfully out of the hut.

I spoke with unreasonable confidence, drawing on reserves of nervous energy.

"Oh no, Lobo," I said. "Nobody else is going to die in Edu because of you. You'll be the next person to die here."

He turned on me with a violent flood of words. I retreated from him as he came towards me. For ten yards he followed me,

172

his voice breaking into falsetto squeaks. Beside himself with fury, he screamed threats at me.

I hastened back along the path to the centre of the village and shouted for the boat.

Reaction came after my confident outburst and that night I was more anxious than ever. I moved restlessly about the deck feeling helpless before some impending catastrophe. I went to my bunk just before midnight; an hour later I was still awake. Loud high-pitched wails came from the village. I came up and stood in pyjamas on the deck. The police and crew were there staring apprehensively towards the beach. I called to Hiro. He came slowly and unwillingly.

"Who's making that noise," I asked.

"Belema's people; he's dying. They say it's your fault."

The cries subsided and I went back to my bunk. An hour later I was on deck again. I found it impossible to sleep. A shimmer of dry lightning momentarily illuminated the water around us and I caught a glimpse of a canoe making its way towards the beach. Someone had visited the *Wai-ai* under cover of darkness.

Next day, except to order food and drink, I spoke to no one. Somehow the day passed and in the late afternoon I went ashore and found myself walking towards the *tabu*-hut and the houses beyond the outskirts of the village. I went as far as the inlet of water running up to the hut. A few women returning from the gardens with yams regarded me curiously, and then looked back doubtfully as they went on their way to the village. I stood irresolute for a moment and then, impelled by some force, I walked slowly towards Lobo's hut. I pushed aside the screen of thatch palm-leaf which barred the opening and walked in. There was a repellent stench which came from a large flat stone encrusted with filth. It was on this stone, I thought, that Lobo cut up the pigs. As I grew accustomed to the dim light I discerned a human skull resting on a small platform of lashed sticks. It was an ancestor shrine like the object I had destroyed at Bagana, but there was no stone before it. A resemblance of skin and flesh were given to the bone by the hardened paste of the titi nut and there were markings on it in charcoal and lime, but here there was no flat stone. The skull was fixed in the wicker-work frame and there was a hole in the top of it. A little light came from the open entrance and I peered into the skull. In it there were pieces of areca nut, taro and yam, and cigarette ends, plum stones from a tin Beni had opened, and an old tooth-brush that I had thrown away the day before. That was all I could make out without delving into the collection of rubbish. On the sandy ground near the entrance to the hut there were two stones. I picked them up. They were of igneous rock which I had not seen before on the island. The bigger stone was marked on its flat surface, where it appeared to have been beaten by the smaller stone. I emerged from the hut in the late afternoon sun and found a small crowd had assembled a little distance away. I walked over the coral shingle to the sea and stood where I had seen Lobo standing two nights before. I beat the stones together and then howled. A dorsal fin broke surface and cleaved the water as an enormous shark swam at great speed towards me. The large, dirty-white body grounded and lay, moving slightly, at my feet. An excited buzz of sound now came from the crowd and I looked round and saw Lobo coming unsteadily over the shingle. Someone must have run to him when I had entered the hut. I prodded the shark with my feet and then spat on it. With a bowling motion I threw the two stones as far as I could out to sea and then turned and walked back to the shingle to face Lobo. We stood about fifteen feet apart. He was a repulsive figure, but more pathetic in his feebleness than frightening. He was trembling violently and gasping for breath, his malevolent old face working as he mouthed meaningless sounds at me. Then I saw his jaw drop and his knees buckle. I got to him before he fell and Hiro and Wetera, in mufti, came out of the crowd to help me. Volunteers joined them and they carried the old man to the hut where I had seen him the night before. He was put down on his bed mat and a dirty old trade blanket was drawn over him. He was limp and breathing stertorously, and his pulse rate was rapid. I was unwilling to leave him in the unventilated evil-smelling hut, but I could think of nothing else to do. I told the women round the hut to do what they could, then I left him and walked back to the village.

With the sudden nightfall of the tropics it had become dark soon after I left the huts; fireflies sparkled along the edge of the path and the night chorus of insect life was in full swing. The stench of decay was stronger by night than by day and I strode hurriedly along, frightened in the darkness of snakes and crocodiles on the path. I went straight to the beach. The boat was there and Gagi and Wesu were waiting. They took me off to the *Wai-ai* smartly without waiting for orders, and then brought the boat carefully alongside for me to get aboard.

I slept better that night than I had done for some time, and I woke up next morning refreshed and fully rested.

There was a cluster of canoes crowding round the *Wai-ai*. Bako was aft, wearing his red sash and khaki *lava lava* and talking animately with Hiro and Wetera. Belema was there too, sitting on the gunwale, looking weak but relaxed and untroubled. Hiro came forward eagerly as soon as he saw me on the deck.

"Have you heard the news?" he exclaimed excitedly. "There is good news."

I disregarded his excited outburst.

"What are all these people here for?" I asked.

Hiro looked aft and then turned to me again with a smile.

"I think they have come to see you because they are happy."

"What is all this about?"

"He's dead, he's dead," Hiro declared gleefully. "Can you hear the drums?"

"Who's dead? What are you talking about?"

"Lobo, sir, He died last night."

Bako, Belema, the remaining police and the visitors from the shore whom I did not know, crowded round Hiro, facing me wide-eyed with excitement.

I smiled at them. "The *tabu*-hut should be burned," I said to

Bako. "Send someone to do that now. Now let me get dressed and have breakfast."

Lobo was not mentioned again when I saw Bako ashore. We discussed tax collection and, as we talked, I saw some elderly people cleaning the ground in the precincts of their huts. Bako told me that five canoes had already left with diving parties; later in the day a large party was setting out in search of turtles. It was breeding time and many were expected to be coming up the beaches on the islands north of Edu.

Men, women and children came down to the waterside and shouted and waved when we left. The tidal stream ran with great velocity along the channel between the islands. For two miles the *Wai-ai* moved slowly; at one point where the channel narrowed she seemed stationary for a few seconds, then she gradually made way and two hours later we emerged on the other side of Ysabel and started our journey down the south coast of the island.

Tarova in ill-fitting uniform and breathless, as though he had hurried to meet me, was at the wharf when we got back to Tataba. He reported that a constable had arrived in a Chinaman's schooner from Tulagi and handed me the letter he had brought. The second paragraph interested me more than the brief note on the constable's posting. Hiro, promoted corporal, was to take over the detachment; Tarova was posted to Tulagi. The *Wai-ai* ran economically on diesel oil; I sent Tarova in her to Tulagi next day. I said Hoile should now sit outside my room at the office and be my orderly.

CHAPTER EIGHT

Discord and Strife

I SPENT the night aboard the *Wai-ai* tied up at the Government Wharf. I had slept late and now I stood on deck sluicing myself with a bucket of water.

The sea had an indeterminate turquoise hue—neither green nor blue but a blend of both. The morning was cool and in the diffused light the craft in the harbour appeared to be riding high out of water and their reflections were mirror-like and still. As I ate breakfast Jenkins the treasurer and his clerks came down the hill to their office. Their starched and stiffly pressed shirts and trousers would become grubby and creased as the day wore on.

Wesu took my suit-case to Melhuish's house and I crossed the wharf to the treasury. Jenkins moved his glasses down his bulbous nose and regarded me with kindly interest. He was about fifty-five and I thought of him as old and wise. He asked me about Tataba, but he did not listen to my reply.

"You ought to get married, that's what you ought to do," he said with a slightly Cockney accent. "You'll get nothing wrong with yourself then."

"There's nothing wrong with me now," I said, but he ignored me and spoke to one of his clerks.

"You get nothing wrong with yourself now, do you?" he demanded.

I met Bingham as I left the treasury. He greeted me in an extravagant manner.

"Golf tonight?" he asked as he turned to go.

"No clubs," I said.

"I've got a spare set."

"Right, thank you."

"Half-past four?"

"Right."

The path to Darcy's office left the waterside path at an acute angle and climbed sharply. Sweat poured down my face and red colouring from my tie ran into my sodden shirt.

Darcy was drafting a long letter to Fiji, but he enquired about my health and asked whether I was worried by anything. As an afterthought he added: "You may be interested in a service at the Court House at eight o'clock on Sunday morning." I thanked him and went out to the main office.

"Mrs Kelsey has asked us to dinner tonight," Melhuish said when I joined him at lunch.

"Are you sure she wants me to come?"

"She particularly wants you to come. We are going to the Club dance afterwards."

"Is Kelsey going to the dance?"

"I believe so."

I turned right through the cutting thirty yards short of the treasury to the small coarse-grassed cricket ground on the other side, past the bachelors' quarters with the lines of drying laundry, and so on to the white-painted Club building. The golf-course lay beyond in an expanse of flat land surrounded on three sides by heights and on the fourth by the sea. Bingham boomed a facetious greeting when he saw me. He cultivated a manner to conceal imperfect self-assurance. His well-tailored clothes and his deeply engraved signet ring were part of the character he had made for himself. Maybe on account of hidden uncertainties he was sensitive to slights and bitterly resisted assaults on his self-esteem. I took him at his own valuation and found him a friendly good-hearted man, and I knew too much about him to underrate his competence.

Bingham won hole after hole, criticising my shots with jocular understatement. "A little oblique," he said when I
178

drove in the wrong direction; "A slight slice," he suggested when the ball shot away into a clump of ivory nut palms. At the eighth hole, the longest on the course, Bingham's drive went two hundred yards straight down the fairway; I drove just as straight fifty yards farther. Bingham's second shot dropped short of the bunker. I played a number six iron hard and true and the ball soared and then dropped and stopped on the hard packed sand a foot from the hole. I holed in three—two less than Bingham. As we walked back to the ninth tee, Bingham cleared his throat. "Fowler," he said, "have you been saved?" There had been ribald comment on Bingham's association with an evangelical missionary, but I was unprepared for his question.

"I beg your pardon," I said.

"Have you been saved?" he repeated.

I had recovered from my surprise.

"No, have you?" I asked.

We had come to the ninth tee. Bingham cleared his throat again.

"No, not yet, but I'm awaiting a call. It's your honour," he said.

I topped my drive into the bunker; Bingham's tee shot pitched on the sand and he holed in two. I picked up my ball and we went into the Club. Four or five people—Jones among them—sat at a table loaded with beer bottles. There was a whisper and a snigger as we passed.

Bingham changed into brown-and-white buckskin shoes. He pulled on a lemon-coloured jersey, knotted a silk square at his neck, fluffed up the hair at his temples and went out on to the verandah. We sat at a table close to the rail, looking out to the west. Bingham put a cigarette in a long holder and a Club boy brought us whiskies and sodas. We watched the sun as it disappeared like a fiery red ball behind the horizon.

A second round of drinks was brought to us and Bingham lit another cigarette. He would have one more drink before dinner, he told me, and smoke his last cigarette after dinner.

"I expect to have more," I said. "I am dining with the Kelseys."

"Kelsey!" he exclaimed with distaste. "The man's a soaker. Certain standards are expected of a gentleman; Kelsey's behaviour falls short of them. I've got no time for him." He pursed his lips as though in disapproval.

Bingham gave great weight to commonplace utterances. He had a way of leaning over the table with his head poised and of speaking confidently as though with special authority.

"What have you planned for your future?" he asked me.

"I haven't thought about it," I said.

"You should, my dear fellow, you should. What you must do is get a transfer from this place and there will then be nothing to stop you bob bob bobbing along like the robin." Bingham looked at his watch. "It's quarter-past seven," he said abruptly, no longer interested in me. "I must go." He stood up and put his cigarette-holder in his pocket. "Good-night to you and thank you for the game." He walked off with a swagger, bidding people good-night as he passed them on the Club verandah. I heard him whistling as he followed his caddy who carried a lamp before him across the golf-course to his house.

Kelsey was a man of unsuspected attainments. His degree and professional qualifications were so good that it was difficult to say what had brought him to the Solomons. He read a lot and had lately taken to painting in oils. He had shown a liking for me. Twice, out of respect for his knowledge and age, I had allowed myself to be trapped into drinking with him at Chow Kai's store. I had sat with him in the squalid room of the Chinaman's store while the late afternoon sun had shone outside and people had gone to the Club to play tennis or golf. I had listened with absorbed attention to his far-reaching talk.

On a recent occasion Kelsey had fallen asleep and had been sick at the Residency, and he had been carried ashore from a party in a visiting gunboat. Everyone knew he had been sternly warned and now, to anyone who would listen, he displayed a morbid animosity towards Darcy.

Melhuish and I were the last to arrive that evening. Hardy, the radio engineer, and his wife were there, Hever, a new nursing sister named Miss Firth, a dark vivacious girl from Bundaberg, Cantle, the entomologist, a couple named Lingard from Guadalcanal, and a Mrs Pellew who was staying with the Kelseys.

Mrs Kelsey seemed pleased to see me. "There's an empty chair by Ted; sit there," she said. Kelsey, red faced and bloated, slurred some of his words when he spoke. He asked me what I had been doing. I told him that I had played golf with Bingham.

"You played golf with Bingham!" he exclaimed.

"Yes, why not?"

"I can't understand you. The man's got the mentality of a shop-walker; he's a mountebank."

"He's all right."

"All right, Bingham all right!" Kelsey was almost shouting and his wife looked towards him anxiously.

"Never mind Bingham," I said. "Tell me about the gun-running into Malaita during the labour trade with Queensland."

"Why do you want to know about that?" he asked suspiciously.

"I'm interested."

"On the Malaita coast the natives used to fire on the boats of recruiting ships; for a long time sailors were killed every year there," Kelsey said. "They used to speak of it as death by natural causes in the Solomons."

"Yes, so I've been told," I said. "But how did the Malaita men get their firearms?"

"At first they were openly sold for produce in trading stores; traders bought the protection of a chief with firearms and then traded them for shell and *bêche-de-mer*. Sailing-ships from Sydney came down and took the stuff away. When the Navy stopped the open trade, rifles were brought in by Queensland recruiting ships."

"There was a regular traffic in firearms then?"

"Certainly," he said. "They were brought in by every returning ship."

"With white men getting shot, you'd have thought every-one would have been against it."

"There was a lot of money in it. The Navy searched ships, but plenty of guns went ashore at Malaita. Government came here in 1897 and the Resident Commissioner, Woodford, did what he could. Rifles were found in the bunt of sails, in galley funnels, lashed to ships' tops and tied to fishing-lines held overboard. The crews were always mixed up in it and got cunning at finding new hiding places."

Kelsey had drunk two strong whiskies while he was talking to me, and he must have had more before we arrived. He swayed a little in his chair.

"Did the traffic in firearms cease when the Queensland labour trade ended in 1903?" I asked.

"Recruiting for Queensland ended in 1903," Kelsey corrected me. "There were ships bringing back labourers for ten years after that, and even when they stopped, firemen in steamers coming up here landed rifles."

We had exhausted the subject and conversation began to flag.

"An old man in the Russell Islands told me he had been blackbirded to New Caledonia and was away for five years. It is hard to picture people taken away against their will," I said.

Kelsey grunted. "Plenty were taken; curiosity got them into trouble."

"In what way?"

"They used to go out when they saw a schooner, then someone stove in their canoe and they were in the water. . . ."

He suddenly stopped. I had heard a remark from Lingard about Darcy visiting his place on Guadalcanal.

"Darcy!" Kelsey exclaimed. "I won't have that name mentioned in this house."

"Don't be a fool, Ted," his wife said. "You can't stop people talking about Mr Darcy just because you don't like him."

Kelsey's face seemed to swell; he looked very angry.

"He's a rat-faced bounder."

"A bounder is the last thing you'd call Mr Darcy."

"The man's a rat-faced bounder, I tell you."

Mrs Kelsey was patient and she was among friends, but her voice had a slight edge.

"I don't think you'd say that to Mr Darcy's face," she said. Kelsey pulled himself to his feet.

"No?" he said with a rising inflexion, walking across the room. Mrs Kelsey looked at him with concern.

"Where are you going, Ted?" she asked.

Kelsey went down the verandah steps to the lawn in front of the house. He turned and faced the Residency, which stood about two hundred yards away on higher land. He put his hands round his mouth.

"You're a rat-faced bounder," he shouted.

A boy hurried out of the house to see what was wanted. Kelsey ignored him and shouted again.

"You're a rat-faced bounder."

A dog in a house across the cutting began to howl. Mrs Kelsey came to the top of the steps.

"Don't be a fool, Ted," she said. "Come in."

But once again Kelsey put his hands round his mouth.

"Darcy, you're a rat-faced bounder," he shouted. He then turned and came up the steps into the house. None of the guests showed by a sign that anything unusual had happened. Kelsey was panting when he sat down again in his chair.

We returned to the sitting-room after dinner to drink coffee and brandy. It was a room made pleasant by attractive curtains and cushions and by rugs on the polished floor. Kelsey's books were ranged on shelves made specially for them and two of his canvases hung on the walls; elsewhere there were good reproductions. Mrs Kelsey had arranged flowers with skill. The garish light of oil lamps was subdued with pink silk shades. I would have been content to stay where we were, but at half-past ten Mrs Kelsey said it was time to go to the Club. Kelsey was not now expected to come, but when we got up to go, he joined us. We walked in couples down the graded coral-metalled paths to the golf-course. We could hear the dance music as we walked across the course to the Club. Coconut-palm fronds fixed along the verandah, a crudely fashioned archway of foliage over the entrance and sprays of purple bougain-villaea displayed in corners of the building and tied against the

walls, all failed in their purpose. They were not decorative—
they merely gave the Club a raffish and untidy appearance.
Kelsey and Hardy left us as soon as we arrived, but the rest of
the men danced in turn with the women on the Club verandahs.

There were twice as many men as women at the dance and
the women, warm and moist in the still close night, danced
heroically time after time to the gramophone music. The
sweating, animated crowd grew boisterous as the night
advanced. The Club boys brought us drinks to the table outside, where we sat watching the incoming tide washing over
the coral shark-barrier at the bathing-pool. A canoe, lazily
paddled, passed close in shore, making for one of the islands.
No one in our party wanted to dance any more. The shimmering moon-lit water was peaceful and we talked of trivialities as
we sipped our drinks.

By midnight the Club boys were too busy to come out to
us. I mounted the steps, and carrying a tray with our empty
glasses dodged between the dancers along the back verandah
to get more drinks. There was something wrong in the bar.
It was a small room—little more than a dispense hatch—but
some people preferred standing there to sitting at tables on the
verandah. Lucas was there. The night before he had talked
familiarly of beauties whose portraits I had seen in the illustrated
magazines. He had told me of the strange eccentricities of
notable judges, of the Cavendish Hotel, of musical shows on the
London stage and of other topics of the moment. I had envied
him his good looks and self-assurance and the life of self-
indulgence he seemed to have led in London. Lucas now stood
as though he were pressed back against the wall at the end of
the little room. Ah Sui, the barman, peered over the bar, tiny
and afraid. Jones, Warner of the Customs and Hardy looked
uncomfortable and almost ashamed. Kelsey, sitting in a wicker
chair at the other end of the room, was talking drunkenly. He
was remonstrating with Hector Pratt, whose exuberant vitality
and powerful body dominated the company. Pratt ignored
him and in his mellifluous slow-speaking voice abused Lucas,
uttering unforgivable filthy insults with careful deliberation.

Lucas, tight-lipped, his eyes light blue and slightly protuberant in his pink flushed face, looked back desperately.

Bingham, carrying three empty glasses on a tray, came into the bar.

"I say, what's going on here?" he demanded peremptorily.

Pratt turned slowly towards him.

"Get out," he said.

Bingham blustered pompously.

"Who do you think you are addressing?"

"Get out."

Bingham hesitated and started to speak again.

"Out," Pratt commanded.

When Bingham went Pratt glanced at me as though he were about to speak, but changed his mind. He picked up his glass, drank and renewed his abuse of Lucas. He wore a black tie and white jacket; he must have been someone's guest, but he looked immense, uncouth and repulsive. I tapped his shoulder.

"Stop that," I said.

Unhurried and calmly he faced up to me. "Shut up," he said, and then, as though he had disposed of my objections, turned again to Lucas.

I clutched his arm. A smaller man would have swung round with the tug I gave, but Pratt, showing growing annoyance, merely turned his head and looking at me with contempt gave me the same foul abuse that he had directed at Lucas. Then, with a grimace, as though I were of no account, he turned to Lucas again.

There was a brief silence, and in the charged atmosphere of the little room I saw with heightened perception the lead-lined ice-box where beer was cooled, bottles of whisky and gin on the shelf behind, tins of Capstan cigarettes stacked like a pyramid, and Ah Sui, small and forlorn, with his hands palm up on the bar. The gramophone music outside seemed far away. As he turned away, I hit Pratt with a heavy right-hand punch, a hard punch to his chin with the jarring impact of bone on bone. His arms hung helplessly at his sides. He gaped at me with surprise and he may have been a little drunk. A film of red clouded my vision. In a surge of fury I hit his face repeatedly with all my strength and weight, vicious overhand jabs with right and left fists.

Hardy and Warner held my arms. "That's enough, that's enough," I heard Hardy say. "You'll kill him."

I stood back and then on an impulse I went for Pratt again, putting an arm lock on him and pushing him out of the bar and along the verandah to the top of the main Club steps. I released my grip and kicked him. He stumbled helplessly down the steps and, catching a foot at the bottom, he sprawled full length, and lay face down and motionless on the coral-gravel path outside. I remained where I was until he slowly got to his feet and came unsteadily back up the steps to me. He was bleeding freely from cuts on his forehead and below each of his eyes. His white clothes, soiled by the dirty gravel, were saturated with blood. He was like a ghastly illustration in a medical law book.

"You put a foot inside this Club and you'll get it again," I warned him.

He stood under the archway of greenery at the entrance, his mouth working silently. Then with difficulty he spoke.

"I'll get you, Fowler," he said venomously. "I'll get you if it's the last thing I do; I'll cut your bloody throat. I won't forget you."

"Go away," I told him. "Go back to your schooner and wash your face."

There was no one left on the Club verandahs. At the first sign of disorder everyone had fled and someone had taken Kelsey away. Jones had gone too, but Hardy, Warner and Lucas were waiting for me in the bar. I was unmoved by their congratulations; I only felt remorse. I had lost control of myself and had behaved in a bestial manner. I had joined in a pot-house brawl; nothing could undo that.

"Someone ought to see if Pratt's all right," I said.

Warner gulped the remains of his drink. "I'll go," he said. He took his torch from Ah Sui and went out.

Darcy was displeased by our intrusion. It was Sunday morning and he sat in a deck-chair on the Residency verandah with a pile of newspapers beside him. I had decided that he should hear first about the brawl from me. Lucas came with me up the hill and stood at my side as I made a formal request for an interview.

"Come into the office," Darcy said quietly.

He was apprehensive as he sat facing us over his desk. Only a matter of the utmost urgency could justify an intrusion at that hour and day.

"There was a disturbance in the Club last night," I said.

He gave me no help.

"Oh," he replied, regarding me with close attention.

"I had to hit someone."

Alarm showed in his face.

"You haven't killed anyone?"

"Oh no, he's just cut about rather badly."

Darcy looked interrogatively from me to Lucas.

"What's this all about?" he demanded.

Lucas intervened. "Fowler was protecting me from an extremely offensive attack," he said.

"From whom?"

"A man named Pratt," I said.

"The gross creature with long black hair and a large mouth?"

"Yes, sir."

"You beat up that man?"

"Yes, sir."

Darcy appeared to be relieved. He pushed cigarettes towards us and smiled.

"Good for you," he said. "It's about time that man had a good hiding."

The interview was taking an unexpected course.

"There have been a lot of complaints about Pratt," Darcy went on, "but the police can pin nothing on him."

He looked at me with amused interest.

"You gave him a real pasting?"

"Yes, sir, a real pasting."

He laughed. "Don't make a habit of it," he said, and then his face clouded.

"Is he a member of the Club?"

"I understand he's not," Lucas replied.

"Who's the secretary?"

"Jones is, I believe," Lucas said.

"Ah yes."

Darcy made a note on a scribbling-block and then looked at the desk clock.

"Ten o'clock," he said. "Not too early for a glass of beer."

We went back to the verandah. A servant filled three tankards from a jug of beer. After the late night and the walk up the hill, the cold bitter beer was immensely refreshing.

Darcy walked with us to the top of the steps.

"Avoid brawls in future," he said to me. "If it happens again, an entry will be made in your file, and that won't do you any good."

I went to the bachelors' quarters with Lucas.

Three people, still in pyjamas, were sitting outside their rooms. They shuffled along the verandah towards us when they saw us come in. Twining, a clerk in Jenkins' office, his hair wet, wrapped in a towel and just out of a shower bath, joined them. He regularly exercised with a barbell and I had seen him grip a vertical stanchion and hold his body horizontal.

"How do you train?" he enquired seriously.

McNab, the junior surveyor, stared with open-eyed wonder. "They say you threw him over the verandah rail," he exclaimed.

Miles, an older man, still unshaven though it was eleven o'clock, smiled. "That clip of yours must have been a beaut," he declared. "Pratt weighs all of eighteen stone. How did you get him?"

The whole affair was preposterous and my own position absurd.

"I hit him on the chin when he wasn't looking," I said.

They laughed, as though even a poor joke of mine required it.

"I did, I tell you," I repeated. "He turned his head and stuck out his chin into my fist."

I left them and pushed open the spring door of Lucas's room and went in. As I lay on the bed I heard them talking outside. Profane exclamations of wonder showed that Lucas's embroidered account of the affray was being well received.

The burst of chatter petered out when someone in heavy shoes walked noisily along the verandah. "He's in there," I heard Lucas say.

"Can I come in?" someone asked, and then Warner peered round the door.

I sat on the edge of the bed. "Of course," I replied. "Come in."

"Crichton wants to see you at twelve noon without fail."

"What for?"

"Search me."

"It's about Pratt, I suppose."

"I don't know."

"What happened last night?"

"I took him to the hospital. Miss Firth cleaned him while I went for Crichton."

"Crichton must have cursed you."

"He wasn't too pleased; he was in bed."

Crichton looked at me with sardonic amusement.

"What have you been up to?" he asked, taking my hands and feeling them. "No fingers broken?"

"I don't think so."

"You are all right?"

"Oh yes, I'm all right. How's Pratt?"

Crichton reached for a bottle of iodine on the shelf behind him. My raw knuckles smartened painfully as he daubed them. He dropped the cotton wool into a pedal bin. He washed his hands in a corner basin and took a towel to dry himself.

"Pratt?" he grunted. "I put twelve stitches in his face last night. He was put to bed here, but walked out this morning. I saw the *Wayfarer* pass an hour ago."

His face softened into a smile when I thanked him as I turned to go.

"Avoid Pratt," he advised. "He said a lot of unpleasant things about you last night."

Lang's Chinese mechanic was dissatisfied with the *Wai-ai's* engine and I was unable to leave Tulagi on Monday as I had planned. The delay was the more irksome as both in the Club and in the offices I visited I was repeatedly asked about what had happened that night in the Club. People wanted to know what Bingham had done when he had walked into the bar. The malicious rumours which had circulated had their origin, I suspected, in gossip by Kelsey, though his drunken mumbling at Pratt had been no less ignoble than Bingham's behaviour.

Nothing was said against the onlookers in the bar; it was Bingham who was generally denounced, the more so because it was vaguely asserted he had somehow failed in his duty. For three nights I did not see him at the Club; he must have had a compelling reason for keeping away as he was an enthusiastic golfer. He may have heard a whisper of what was being said about him, but it was more likely that he was worried by the thought that he had been humiliated by Pratt and felt disinclined to meet people.

At midday on Thursday a note came from Darcy inviting me to dinner that evening. He asked me for seven o'clock, which was early.

The Residency, when the Darcys were there, was a well-regulated household where humour, friendliness and warm hospitality were to be found. Whenever I was in Tulagi I dined at the house and as often as not, stayed there.

I changed into a white dinner-jacket and a black tie and walked along the ridge path from Melhuish's house. It was ten minutes to seven. Early, I thought, but something had been said about a drinks party before dinner.

Darcy was alone; his wife had gone home to find a house for their leave. He had just come up from the Club when I arrived. "Bingham's coming in," he said. "I'll change after he goes."

White-painted cane chairs were arranged in one corner of the verandah; a silver cigarette-box, a tray of drinks and an assortment of glasses stood on a low table.

"How well do you know Bingham?" Darcy asked when I sat down.

"Fairly well," I said. "I played golf with him on Saturday."

"Do you like him?"

"Yes."

"I'm glad of that; I can make nothing of him at all. He refuses our invitations here; I'm glad he's coming at last. He's taking this affair at the Club very much to heart, I'm told, and there's this gossip about him. He does his work as well as anyone, and that is all that interests me."

I wondered who told Darcy things, but I said nothing.

"Is there anyone else coming, sir?" I asked.

"No, only Bingham now. Jenkins and Crichton are coming later for dinner and bridge.

Wire baskets with orchids hung overhead and ferns in tubs were ranged along the verandah. Darcy's boy dropped cubes of ice into my drink with tongs from a wide-mouthed vacuum flask. Darcy lighted my cigarette and then in the failing light looked down the terraced garden where the steps came up to the house from the bed of cannas below. "Good God," he suddenly exclaimed and got up. He stood at the top of the verandah steps when Bingham came up. He was in uniform; an orderly followed him with a brief-case.

Bingham saluted. "You ordered me to be here at 1915 hours," he reported.

"Take your hat off and come and sit down," Darcy said quietly. "I didn't order you to do anything; I invited you here for a drink."

Bingham said nothing. He pursed up his mouth and looked undecided. Darcy stared at the orderly.

"Must this fellow stay?" he asked.

"He's brought some files I thought I might want," Bingham said.

"Files?"

191

Bingham cleared his throat: "I was not aware of the subjects you wished to discuss with me."

"Bingham," Darcy said, articulating carefully, "do you mind sending this man away?"

"Well, sir, I'm not sure . . ." Bingham started to say.

Darcy interrupted him. "Take off your tunic and sit down. Do what I say, there's a good fellow," he said firmly. "If you want to argue about anything, let's leave it until the morning. What will you have to drink?"

Bingham became unsure of himself. He looked miserable.

"May I have a whisky and soda?" he asked.

"You may," Darcy replied, and poured him out nearly three fingers, and added soda, before Bingham could protest.

"Take your tunic off and relax," Darcy urged him.

Bingham began to object. "Go on, Bingham, take it off," Darcy went on. "You can't drink like that."

Bingham took off his tunic and laid it carefully over the back of a chair. He sat in long khaki trousers, well-polished brown boots and the cellular weave vest he wore under his tunic. He was not at ease. He looked undressed and sloppy.

The rank absurdity of the affair suddenly appealed to Darcy. He laughed out loud and then immediately apologised.

"I'm sorry, Bingham," he said. "It just struck me as grotesque of you to wear uniform and bring files when I asked you in for a drink." Darcy laughed again.

"Not at all, sir," Bingham said with a slight cough.

Conversation was difficult. Darcy tried hard and I did what I could, but Bingham was taciturn and ill at ease. He got up at half-past seven and firmly refused a second drink. He thanked Darcy and went off in the darkness, carrying his hat and belt.

"You see what I mean?" Darcy said reflectively when Bingham had gone. "I asked the man here because I hear he's being treated badly and to show him he has my support, and that's the way he behaves. When Kelsey came here he dropped a cut-glass decanter, vomited, and then fell asleep."

The schooner had come round Fulakora Point and instead of

keeping out to sea on the normal course for Tulagi she had changed course and had headed for Tataba. I watched her curiously from the office door. The wind had gone round to the north on her beam and she was making good time across the bay. She looked a comfortable handy rig; her mainsail, and then her foresail came crumpling down into a heap on her deck and her engine drove her forward towards the passage in the reef. Hoile came out and joined me and stood staring intently at the schooner. "*Wayfarer!*" he suddenly exclaimed.

"*Wayfarer*; that's Hector Pratt's."

"Yes."

I identified the vessel as soon as he spoke. I had seen her in Tulagi harbour with Pratt, half-naked, moving about on deck, but I had never seen her on the Ysabel coast. I wondered what had brought her away from her usual business between Tulagi, Malaita and Guadalcanal; I wondered more what was bringing her into Tataba and the possibility that Pratt might prove violent occurred to me. It was five or six months since the incident in the Club and I had not seen him in that time and I had sometimes wondered what would happen when I did meet him. I had been impressed by Crichton's warning and did not belittle the risk of a fight. There was not much he could do against Hoile and me, but I could not help being uneasy as I heard the anchor chain run out down below in the harbour. I returned to my chair to wait for him. Ten minutes later I heard voices outside and Hoile told me Pratt had arrived.

"Tell him to come in," I said.

Pratt wore only shorts and slippers. As I looked at his massive bare chest and enormous shoulders and arms I marvelled at my temerity in hitting the man. I stood up and gestured towards the chair as he walked slowly across the room towards me. "Sit down," I said.

I looked at him warily, wondering what had brought him. There was a scar under each of his eyes; one was a livid streak with stitch marks on either side. Pratt lowered himself awkwardly on to the chair. He was in no hurry to state his business.

He brought out a flat tin of tobacco and rolled a cigarette. He then held the tin out to me.

"Care for the makings?" he asked.

I shook my head. "No thank you," I replied, still watching him closely.

"It's five years since I was here last," he said after he had lighted the cigarette and put away the tin. He gazed about the room. "This place was new then."

He was not deliberately conciliatory: there was nothing unusual in his manner. He might have been any trader or recruiter calling at Tataba on his way to Tulagi. He was far more at his ease than I was as he went on talking equably about a man named Bailey who, he said, had lived and worked in the office before the house on the hill was built. I barely listened to him. I was still uneasy. I could not make out what he was driving at.

"What's brought you out here?" I asked when I got the chance.

"Labourers for Berryman, and I'm going back with copra from Cullen."

"You're on your way to Tulagi now?"

"Yes, back to the capital."

I waited to hear what he wanted.

"You've got a boy here called Folami?"

Folami was bigger and darker-skinned than Soge, but they belonged to the same kindred group. He had held good jobs but his last employer, a recruiter named Pilling, had left the Islands and he had been living on the station for about a month.

"Yes, he's been here since Pilling left."

"What's he like?"

"I don't know. Do you want to see him?"

"Yes, I'll give him a look over as I'm here."

Pratt was a notorious character; everyone knew about him. Folami could decide for himself whether he wanted to work for him.

Pratt got up and walked about the room.

"Yes, it was here Bailey and me made a night of it."

He whistled as he peered at the window frames and tested the corner posts with his hands.

"I've got a couple of spare bottles of booze you can have if you're short," he said.

"I've got plenty, thanks," I said.

White visitors to Tataba were rare and their arrival was something of an occasion. I usually invited them to the house for a drink or a meal; and there were some to whom I offered a bed. Pratt's relaxed manner and melodious slow-speaking voice was disarming. I found myself worried by his familiarity. If he thought at all about the beating I had given him, he showed no sign of it until for the barest instant he was off guard and a malevolent, cunning, shifty expression came over his face—a look of keen appraisal, that was gone in a flash. I resisted his show of amiability until Hoile announced that Folami had come. Folami accepted Pratt's offer and went back to the hut on the beach for his bedroll and box. I got Pratt out of the office by offering to walk with him as far as the wharf. I refused his invitation to drink in the *Wayfarer*. That was the last time I saw him. The schooner had gone when I looked down from the house in the morning.

Two months later, when I visited Tulagi, people in Elkington's Hotel and at the Club were still talking about Pratt's death. I heard no regret expressed, no one was saddened by his death, but its violence, its unexpectedness and its circumstance had shocked people along the waterfront.

It had happened a week before. Pratt was due to leave for Malaita, but for three days and nights he had stayed drinking at Sterling's Hotel. An ugly scene on the last night—a man named Payne, insulted and humiliated beyond endurance, had burst into tears and had provoked Pratt to shouts of scornful laughter—had disgusted even the hard, insensitive men who frequented the place and there was relief when the *Wayfarer's* engine sounded at eight o'clock next morning.

I was not interested enough to read the inquest proceedings in Darcy's office. I learned what happened from what people told me. The engine had stopped after a minute and Pratt could be heard cursing his crew; then he had lowered himself over the stern of the schooner. The propeller had been fouled by a line or the packing in the stern glands had been loose. The point was disputed, but it was not important. Pratt had worked on the propeller and the bo'sun leaning over the stern had passed his orders back to the engine room. The engine had stopped and started spasmodically; no one had been concerned until there had been a loud shriek and the sea round the stern of the schooner had been discoloured with blood. The bo'sun and two others of the crew had jumped into the water, but Pratt's body had been too heavy to lift into the dinghy. They had got it to the beach and with the help of two natives who had run to meet them, they had lifted the body on to the path. The heavy blades of the *Wayfarer's* screw had beaten two or three times into Pratt's face and head.

Some people asserted that he had still been drunk and had taken foolish risks, but there was a small lingering doubt about orders that had been given to the engine room. The bo'sun gave a faltering account of what had happened. First he said there had been no order, but later, when he was pressed, he said he thought he had asked for the engine to go slow ahead. The picture was of Pratt shouting abuse and contradictory orders from the water. The bo'sun admitted reluctantly that he might have been confused and might have given the wrong order. This was the coroner's opinion. Folami had declared that the orders he had received from the bo'sun were for full speed astern. He was calm and unshaken when questioned, and his version was accepted in preference to the bo'sun's.

I went right round the island when I got back to Tataba, nearly four hundred miles. I was away three weeks. It was Folami who caught the line when we came into the wharf to tie up.

In the morning the weather was boisterous. The south-east trades had freshened and threatened the thatch of the office roof. Over the reef, where the surf broke with a pulsating roar, high-flung spray hovered like a mist; beyond, as far as I could see, the sea was turbulent. I felt satisfaction at having got back before the worst of the blow.

Soge brought Folami to the office at ten o'clock. He asked permission for him to live in the *Wai-ai* until he found work again.

"Why have you come back?" I asked Folami. "Someone will soon buy the *Wayfarer* and there will be work for you again."

Soge looked at Folami, but he did not answer at once.

"I no want work for *Wayfarer* again," he said at length. "I want job in some other schooner."

I understood his aversion to the *Wayfarer* and said nothing. I considered their request and wondered if there were any objections to it, and then I recalled the laughing light-skinned girl Folami had had with him when he stayed before on the station.

"What about your wife?" I asked Folami.

The door slammed with a noise like a pistol shot. I told Hiro to bolt it and make sure that all the windows and doors were secure.

I repeated my question to Folami.

"What about your wife?"

A look of pain came into his face. Soge glanced at him uneasily, but neither spoke.

"Is the girl still here?" I asked.

Folami had regained his composure. He made an involuntary gesture suggesting the matter was unimportant.

"No, she's not here," he said in a hard toneless voice.

Soge looked away embarrassed, but added, as though he thought I ought to know more, "Folami has sent her back to her village; he no want her again."

It was no business of mine, but I wondered what mischief the girl had got into. I regarded Folami meditatively.

"You no want this fine girl any more; what's wrong?"

His face tightened. "Hector Pratt take her and give her plenty cloth and beads."

I gasped with surprise.

197

"Pratt take your wife?"

"Yes, he say he want her and she go to him."

Folami spoke with unexpected vehemence, and the effect of his words was startling. I felt a chill of horror and my stomach turned over as though I were going to be sick. I shifted in my chair. The two men stood waiting for my reply. Neither moved nor uttered a sound. I looked at Folami. I saw him as a well-mannered, hard-working native. The notion was monstrous. There had been an inquest and Longman had made a full enquiry; he had been days taking statements, I was told. For half a minute I said nothing and the silence became tense and uncomfortable. Then there was a shattering sound and the glass in the window behind me fell tinkling to the bamboo floor. A fast-flying bird caught in a strong gust of wind lay dying on my table with blood seeping from its beak. Folami picked it up and with his left hand stroked the feathers over its head.

"Is it dead?" I asked.

"It's neck is broken, close up die now," he said, looking intently at the bird.

"Let me see it."

He handed me the bird gently. I felt the slightest flicker of life in it. It had a long tail and wings like a swallow. Hoile had come in at the sound of the breaking glass and the three men looked with concern at the bird in my hand.

There was no second quiver.

"It's dead." I gave it to Hoile. "Put it outside," I told him.

"I like to *kai kai* it."

They laughed, and that ended our common concern with the bird.

"All right, take it," I said.

He took the bird with him to his table in the passage.

I turned again to Folami.

"You want to sleep in the *Wai-ai*, you say?"

"Yes, until I get job again."

"Give him some work," I told Soge, "and he can stay there for the present."

I dismissed them and they left me.

CHAPTER NINE

The Woman from Sydney

WE were making for Bala-Bala. We went through the passage in the barrier reef, between two islands and among a litter of coral heads and patches to an anchorage in front of a shed. Cullen was waiting on the beach for me. He took my hand and I jumped stiffly down to the sand when we grounded. He greeted me agreeably. He was a handsome man with slightly over-long dark hair, a pale complexion, lively brown eyes and a mobile expressive mouth. He was about fifty years old. It was late afternoon and he was wearing clean white drill.

"Come up to the house," he said.

I walked with him from the beach along a sandy stone-edged path to a hybrid structure of palm-leaf thatch and corrugated iron.

"You're just in time for a cup of tea. Go up," he said when we came to the steps. The house shook as I walked over the rough-hewn floor boards. The place was filthy with years of dirt. I could see coarse foul sand through gaps in the floor.

We sat on chairs with the tea tray on a box between us and talked for half an hour; then I enquired about the plantation.

"How many labourers have you got?" I asked him.

"Labourers?—none. That is not quite true; I've got a boss-boy and a couple of roustabouts."

"Aren't you making copra?"

"We make a bit. The Koseo people come for a couple of weeks before the *Mahaga* is due and we get a load ready. I can't afford to keep labourers full time."

"The place is going down a little?"

"Yes, I can't help it. My brother and I put all the money we could spare into it and I still have to ask him for more occasionally. He is getting nothing out of it and I am just able to exist here."

I grunted sympathetically and he went on.

"I have to stay here; it's all I possess. Copra was called the 'Consols of the East'—safe as the Bank of England, they said." He laughed. "Look at it today—everyone in the red and not a sign of an improvement in the price. But we must hope for better times. Would you like a bath?"

I stood on a patch of cement in the out-house. Cullen's boy had filled a four-gallon tin, hauled seven feet up by a pulley. By pulling a wire I controlled the water that cascaded over me as I washed. Cullen was lighting a hurricane lamp when I came back into the house. "This is a villainous light," he said. "There is something wrong with the wick, but I never remember until night time."

We ate supper by a poor flickering light. Cullen had opened tins of food with generous hospitality.

"You oughtn't to have done this," I said.

He laughed. "I enjoy a change of *kai kai*. I don't bother unless there is someone here, and that doesn't happen often. I am ashamed that I have nothing to offer you to drink."

There was a gramophone with an immense wooden horn in a corner of the room. After the meal Cullen filled his pipe. "Would you like some music?" he asked.

He handled his records with great care and repeatedly replaced the fibre point in the sound box.

The moon had come up—it was almost a full moon—and a swathe of sea widening to the horizon threw up a glittering silvery reflection. We had sat for hours barely speaking, and moving only to change records.

"What's the time?" I asked.

Cullen pointed the beam of his torch on the clock.

"It's after midnight by me," he said. "You can't go back to the *Wai-ai* tonight."

He carried the lamp to a small box-shaped room with palm-thatch walls. There was a stretcher bed there with a bare expanse of pale green canvas, a chipped enamel wash-basin on a wooden tripod stand, and a large trade box on the floor. Cullen opened the box and took out a mosquito net, sheets and two pillows. They all had a musty smell.

We hung up the net together and then he left me and I made the bed. Half an hour later I was roused from a light sleep by a scuffling sound—rats running over the floor-boards, I thought. Then I heard the clink of clam shell arm-rings and immediately after that the sound of women's voices whispering and hissing in furious dispute. Cullen intervened. He remonstrated and spoke sharply. There was more clinkings of arm-rings, scufflings, and the house shook slightly. Absolute silence followed.

Next morning I met Cullen as he came out of his room. He was freshly shaved and bathed. He grunted a response to my greeting and then sat in silence at the head of the table.

A large pink flesh pawpaw and a slice of lemon was put on a plate for my breakfast. With a sprinkling of sugar it tasted delicious.

"This is like a melon," I said. "It's not a local variety of pawpaw?"

Cullen spooned into his pawpaw without speaking and then poured out a cup of strong coffee for me.

"How did you sleep? Your weren't disturbed in the night?" he asked suddenly.

"Very well, thank you. I had an excellent night."

He relapsed into thoughtful silence and then spoke again.

"You said something about these pawpaws?"

"Yes, they are exceptionally good."

"They are a Javanese variety. I got the seed from Sourabaya. Have you been to Sourabaya?"

"No."

"You ought to go there sometime. There's a wonderful botanical garden there. The Dutch are more enterprising than we are. There's none of this unimaginative devotion to coco-nuts about them."

After breakfast I walked with him over the ill-kept plantation. It was a depressing spectacle, but Cullen was not downcast. Before I left he went into his bedroom and brought out a
pile of issues of the *Illustrated London News, Punch, Blackwood's*
and the *Strand Magazine*.

"Pass these on to anyone who would like them," he
requested.

"What a splendid lot of magazines," I said.

"My sister sends them to me. She's married to a parson in
Cumberland."

The blurred outline of the islands ahead began to take form;
an hour later we entered Huranga Lagoon and went straight
down the fairway to the mission station at the south-east end.
I watched the island approach and saw the native building
with the gravel path down to the waterside. Miss Thompson, a
middle-aged New Zealander, came down the path to meet me.

Funds had been collected somewhere at home for work
among mothers and children. The money was not enough and
Miss Thompson worked under great difficulty. I had called on
her only once before, and I felt a prick of conscience.

We sat in camp chairs at a small table on the springy palm
lath floor.

"Isn't it hard and lonely for you here?" I asked.

"Not as bad as I expected."

"Aren't you scared at night?"

"No, not scared," she laughed. "Petrified."

"Hasn't your attendant a husband—or isn't there a married
couple who could live here?"

"The mission are trying to find a couple for me; in the meantime I sleep with a pair of scissors under my pillow, sharp-
pointed ones." She laughed out loud. "I'd put up a good fight."

A woman servant brought a tray with tea and biscuits and
placed it on the table.

"Are you finding much to do?" I asked.

"Yes, plenty; it would be easier if I had regular clinics, but
the people don't have clocks here."

202

"They come any time of the day?"

"Yes; did you see my flag?"

"I saw a red flag at the top of a bamboo pole."

"I'm supposed to be off duty when the flag's flying."

"I'm sorry," I said. "It was flying when we came."

She laughed. "I don't mind you. I object to being called out of my bath to give a yaws injection or wakened at midnight to see someone who's been sick for years."

I sat another ten minutes wondering how soon I could go. Then I stood up.

"You are sure there's nothing worrying you?" I asked.

"Well," she said gravely, "I didn't want to bother you, but since you ask, there is something."

I had enquired only as a matter of course and I was a little surprised by her reply and by her sudden change of expression. She looked worried.

"Oh," I said. "What's the matter?"

"No one's been here for five days. I've not had a single patient. The place seems to be *tabu*."

"We'll solve the mystery for you," I said confidently, and I told Wetera to make enquiries.

Miss Thompson was effusive in her thanks. She pressed me to stay for a meal.

"Mr Paley brought me three large fish; I could never eat them," she said.

"Is Paley about?"

"Yes, he's over at Diala in the *Daphne*."

A week before at Tataba I had fined Paley £5 for dynamiting fish. He was a plausible rogue, but with some redeeming features. He was good to his native wife and to his brood of half-caste children, and he had often taken men off the beach in Tulagi and kept them at his place for a few months, making them work certainly but allowing them to regain some self-respect.

He was short of food for his crew, he had said, when I had him before me at Tataba, and he had convinced me that he had been driven by force of circumstances to breaking the law. I had made the proceedings as informal as I could. When I was writing out the receipt for his fine he had said he would never dynamite fish again. "I don't want to get into trouble with Government," he had said, "and besides, it's not fair on my crew. There are too many one-armed men about in the Solomons and some have been killed if the truth were known."

I had asked him up to the house for tea and he had shaken my hand warmly when he left. As soon as he had gone, doubts had come into my mind and I thought I had been too lenient with him.

I went straight across the lagoon to the village of Diala, which stood on the waterside in the shadow of a four-thousand-foot mountain.

The *Daphne* was lying there and I saw Paley coming off from the village in his boat. Hoile went ashore and returned immediately. I sent a note to the *Daphne* and told Paley I wanted to see him in the *Wai-ai*. He came at once. He had put on a tie and brushed his hair.

"Why, Mr Fowler, I never expected to see you again so soon," he said.

"Do you want me to subpoena your crew and half the village to prove you've been dynamiting fish again?" I replied.

He looked pained. "I don't want to cause you all that trouble."

"Don't worry about causing me trouble."

He grimaced, as though yielding to unreasonable pressure. "If that's your attitude, there's nothing more to be said."

"What do you mean by that?"

He raised his hands in a gesture. "I won't deny I dynamited a few fish here yesterday. I wanted to take something over to the mission. People don't do enough for Miss Thompson."

"You admit it, then?"

"Oh yes, I admit it. I suppose I must admit it."

He spoke as though making a concession.

"All right then," I told him. "I'm charging you now and the court will sit forthwith."

I went down to the cabin for some foolscap. I had brought no court books with me.

Paley pleaded guilty, but before I sentenced him I formally addressed him.

"There may be people who would be distressed if you were to lose your life or maim yourself in the course of illegal dynamiting. If there are such people, I am not among them. What happens to you is of little consequence to me; but I am concerned with the welfare of the people you employ. I have a duty towards these people to see that they do not suffer injury and that they are not exposed to danger through your wanton criminal folly."

I spoke as sternly as I could and as I went on I caught a glint in Paley's face. He had edged a little down the deck towards me.

"I must warn you with all the force at my command," I concluded, "that if you are found guilty of this offence a third time, you will be sent to prison without the option of a fine." My voice was strong and I spoke confidently. "I am now going to fine you thirty pounds or one month's imprisonment with hard labour."

Paley thrust himself forward before I had finished speaking. He spoke excitedly.

"I like your style, Mr Fowler, I like your style," he declared. "Put it there, put it there." Foolishly I took his hand.

"Thirty quid, did you say? I'll get it now." He went back to the *Daphne* and returned with six *rouleaux* of five pounds in shillings. They were neatly wrapped in brown paper.

"Come over to the *Daphne* for a drink," he suggested.

"No, thank you," I said giving him his receipt.

He lingered in the *Wai-ai* though his boat was alongside waiting.

"No hard feelings, Mr Fowler?" he enquired.

"You'll find out just how hard my feelings are if I have any more trouble from you on this coast," I replied.

"Don't be like that," he said.

I went back to the mission island. Wetera had discovered that an infant had happened to die a day after a yaws injection, and the women had become fearsome. I told Miss Thompson I would tell village headmen to advise their people to come for treatment as they had in the past.

Three weeks after my return to Tataba I went to Tulagi for stores. I left late in the morning and tied up at Government Wharf a little after seven and went ashore to Elkington's Hotel for supper.

Four men were smoking while drinking coffee at the end of the room. Hever was there with them and after a word from him they all looked my way. They asked me when I had arrived and when I was going back and then went on talking among themselves.

Melhuish came in. "Are people coming here now to feed?" I asked, when he sat down with me.

"Yes, Elkington's food is good again," he said.

I drank glass after glass of iced water. It was a luxury for me, and so was the fresh butter that I daubed on my bread.

"Where can I get a canvas bag made?" I asked Melhuish. "The one I used for a punch bag at Tataba got torn."

"Charlie Shatz is a good sail-maker; he'll make you one," he said. "You'll find him hanging round Sterling's Hotel."

I looked at the clock over the door. "It's only half-past nine," I said. "I'll go there now; I'm too restless to turn in."

People from the bar now drifted slowly in and two boys from the kitchen arrived with plates of soup, putting them down as the tables filled. It appeared that Tom, careless for his bar trade, was in a mood for telling people to eat and for refusing them more drink until they did so.

"I'll come with you," Melhuish said.

We walked down the slope to the waterside path, past the offices and the wharf, and then on for a quarter of a mile to a cluster of flimsy wooden shacks with coral jetties leading off to deep water. This was where the Chinese lived—hard-working traders in piece goods, cheap lamps, fish hooks, jews' harps, beads, pipes and gaudy-labelled low-grade tinned food. Their schooners lay at the end of the jetties, discharging trochus shell and copra or loading with trade goods. High-pitched chatter, sibilant exclamations and the clatter of counters disclosed a session of fantan in one of the shacks we passed.

Sterling's Hotel was no better built than the neighbouring Chinamen's stores, but it was bigger. A room with three iron cots, a small dining-room and a kitchen raised the place to the dignity of an hotel.

A babel of noise rose from the fog of tobacco smoke which hung over the bar. The night was sultry and men stood drinking, hairy chested and bare to the waist, wiping away sweat with the trade towels they carried. The lamps, flickering as flying insects got caught in the flames, cast a poor light on the whisky advertisements and the prints of undressed girls displayed in a calamitous attempt to enliven the place.

Melhuish went to the bar and Bandy Coot joined me. "What cheer?" he said. "Have a drink."

"Melhuish is getting me one," I said.

Bandy nodded and stood beside me, mellowed and friendly and talking with a cigarette in his mouth.

"There are six jokers in this room who've been round the Horn in sail," he said. He started to name them but Melhuish came with drinks. He introduced me to Shatz, a small man wearing a sleeveless vest and white drill trousers. He had missed shaving for a day and a white stubble showed on his bony chin. Shatz listened attentively and made suggestions when I told him what I wanted. Koenig who was behind the bar, tall, big-boned man with a hard humourless face, handed him a pencil and paper and he wrote laboriously. The bag would be ready next day he said.

Harvey, a tall fellow with agreeable manners and handsome in a florid fair style, came in with his partner Rankine.

"Have a whisky," Rankine suggested, "it won't hurt you."

Harvey seemed despondent and shook his head. "I'd better have a squash, old boy, if you don't mind," he said.

I pushed through a small group drinking crème de menthe at the bar; they called it starboard lights. As I moved gingerly back through the crowd of jostling drinkers, I heard someone remark, "He asked five pounds for it, but he kicked his arse and took it off him."

"They are talking about a friend of yours," Melhuish said.

"Who's that?" I asked, as I handed Shatz and Bandy, their drinks.

"Paley."

"Is he anybody's friend?"

There was a lull in the babel of drunken talking and singing as a small man, bearded, with tawny sun-bleached hair and a body tanned leathery brick red, a self-satisfied little man, edged past us on his way out. He wore nothing but a pair of tight-fitting shorts.

"He's a Yank off that cutter-rigged job at Carpenters' Wharf," Bandy remarked. "He's sailing round the world."

"By himself?"

"Yes."

Someone near the bar said in a bewildered voice: "I don't get it; what's he doing it for?"

"For money," someone else suggested.

"How's he make money?"

"He'll write a book when he's finished."

"Write a book?"

"Sure, he'll write a book," another man added, "and if he doesn't get free tucker, paint, canvas and anything else he wants, he'll say everyone in Tulagi is a lot of bastards."

There seemed general agreement, and Charlie Koenig observed: "That bugger hasn't paid for a drink since he arrived six days ago."

An elderly man with sweeping moustaches and a jutting jaw stood alone at the bar gazing crossly round the room. He had the style of an old-fashioned actor, but he was a Scandinavian of some sort, a master mariner whose great personal dignity when sober concealed defeat and frustration. Someone chose the wrong moment to speak to him. The old man haughtily looked away.

A record of the waltz tune 'Always' was being played on the gramophone.

I turned at a touch on my back. A long-haired, sallow man stood swaying before me. His clothes were soaked with filth. He stood staring at me, wild-eyed and ill-looking, mouthing with incoherent anxiety. His lips moved soundlessly; and I got the impression that he could not recollect who I was. It was Peter Cullen. The change in the man who had met and entertained me at Bala-Bala was deplorable.

Bandy greeted him: "Hullo Peter, your brother has sent you some money for the plantation again, I see,"

Cullen raised a tremulous forefinger, but Shatz interrupted.

"Go to bed, Peter, go to bed," he told him patiently.

Cullen lurched away and, recognising Harvey, clutched the young man's hand.

"We're the only gentlemen in this place, John," he slurred. "Do you know that?"

"That's right, Peter," Harvey agreed. "Where are you sleeping?"

Cullen waved his hand towards the end of the building.

"O.K., come and show me," Harvey said and led him away.

We came out of Sterling's Hotel at half-past eleven. A slight breeze, no more than a puff of air, came off the land; the sweat cooled on me as we walked slowly back along the path. The water gurgled and murmured under the stones and sometimes there was a tiny splash. A night soil gang on their way round the island with buckets moved silently to one side to allow us to pass. Melhuish turned up the hill at the treasury and I went left to the wharf. Gagi and Wesu had spread out their mats, and despite the wharf light were fast asleep.

In the morning Beni took my suit-case to Melhuish's house. I rested during the afternoon after Melhuish had gone back to work, but got up at a quarter to four to get my canvas bag from Shatz. Johnny Sa'a, bo'sun of the *Tulagi*, was twenty yards ahead of me on the waterside. He wore the petty officer's rig to which he was entitled. On the outskirts of Chinatown a white man staggered drunkenly along the path towards him. He moved with knees bent, making long strides in a grotesque shambling motion. Johnny stopped, apparently offering to help, but the white man ignored him. Johnny looked back, but went on again when he saw me. It was Cullen.

"Did you hear what he called me," he shrieked when he came up to me. "He called me Peter! The bloody black bastard called me Peter." He was almost in tears.

"Come back to the hotel and have a drink," I suggested.

Shatz was at the hotel when we got there. I paid him and rolled up the bag. As I came away I heard him chiding Cullen.

I returned to Tataba next morning and was not in Tulagi again for four months.

There was no wind, and the glare of the sun blazed back from the water and from the white-painted buildings and the path. Across the harbour the harsh whiteness of the strand contrasted sharply with the bright green of the wooded land behind. The *Mataram* had started on her round of the islands. There had been a party in her the night before and I had got to bed late. The morning had been trying, but I had done everything I had come to Tulagi to do and in the hot midday sun I walked wearily up the incline to Elkington's Hotel.

A wide verandah and a well-insulated roof made the place cool. The floors had been scrubbed and the ash-trays were polished and clean. That morning it was quite a good place to be in. There was no one about. It was too early for people who worked in Tulagi. I leaned against the bar with my foot on the rail and gazed round the place while I waited for Tom. Island trophies were displayed on the walls. Clubs, shields, spears and stone-head axes hung in profusion, and there were crescent-shaped body ornaments worked from gold-lipped shell, arm-rings made from clam shells and chiefs' insignia in intricately fretted turtle shell. Tom took my order in silence. He wore a striped cotton shirt with a plain neck-band. His face was shrivelled and lined and his hair and moustache were quite white. He had been more than forty years in New Guinea and South Pacific islands. He prised off the stopper, and froth from the cold beer foamed from the neck of the bottle on to the polished wood bar. Tom pushed the bottle and a glass towards me and wiped up the froth with a cloth. I signed a chit, and he put it away in a drawer.

"There's a lady here asking for you," he said in his gruff old man's voice.

"A lady asking for me?" I said, taken aback.

"Yes, she's off the mail-boat."

I had met women who had stopped off the mail-boat in Tulagi. One had been a dipsomaniac who had refused to leave Sterling's Hotel and had later spent a month in hospital; the others had been trollops free with their favours until they had set up house with someone or had been shipped back to Sydney.

"Off the mail-boat, did you say?" I demanded.

"I know what you're thinking," Tom said severely, "but you're wrong. This is a respectable lady."

I took a swig of beer.

"What does she want?"

He was about to tell me something, but changed his mind.

"She's here; I'll fetch her."

I finished the beer and went out to the verandah, wondering who the woman might be. Tom, walking stiffly, escorted her from a room at the end of the building. She was squatly built with a suggestion of grossness. About forty, her complexion was florid and her eyes were pale blue. She had arranged her light-coloured hair in a plait over her head.

"This is Mr Fowler," Tom growled at her, and then left us together.

She held out a strong square-fingered hand and greeted me with a hard Sydney accent.

"How d'you do?" she said.

Her dress was made of a drab brown patterned material; there was a cheap cameo brooch at her throat. She wore black laced-up town shoes. She was not an intelligent looking woman, I thought, and she was probably lacking in humour. I saw she had a wedding ring.

"Mr Elkington says you want to see me."

"I want to go to Ysabel."

I pointed to the deck-chairs. When she was seated, I offered to get her a drink, but she refused.

I looked at her warily. She seemed out of place in Tulagi.

"Are you a missionary?" I asked.

"No, I'm Mrs Cullen, Mrs Peter Cullen. I want to get to my husband's plantation."

Here were the seeds of trouble for me, I thought.

"You are Mrs Peter Cullen?" I must have sounded incredulous, because she bridled and her voice took on a defiant note.

"Yes I am. We were married four years ago in Sydney."

She opened her bag, and unfolded some paper. "I've got the marriage certificate here if you'd like to see it," she announced.

"Of course not," I said. "I didn't know Peter Cullen was married; that's why I was surprised when you told me. Is he expecting you?"

Doubt showed itself in her face, and she looked at me anxiously.

"I wrote to say I was coming, but I can't be certain if he got the letter. He doesn't write much—in fact he never writes—but I thought there might have been a letter with Mr Elkington for me."

My head had begun to ache. I felt angry with Tom for having drawn me into this affair. I called a hotel boy to take away the hotel cat which had come to me and was clawing my leg. I might have been more tactful and patient if I had not been so tired.

"Mrs Cullen," I said, speaking with great earnestness, "take my advice and stay here while the *Mataram* is in the islands and go back to Sydney when she returns."

She opened her light-blue eyes very wide and looked at me with amazement.

"What are you talking about? After all the expense of coming here from Sydney, you expect me to go back without seeing my husband?"

I sighed. "If he wanted to see you, he would have met you and arranged to get you out to Bala-Bala. I should forget him and go back to Sydney."

212

She rose from the chair and spoke angrily.

"I am not asking you for advice; my affairs are not your business. I am only asking you for transport."

I became conciliatory.

"I'm sorry," I said. "Please sit down. You are quite right, your affairs are nothing to do with me."

She sat upright in the deck-chair with her hands clasped over the bag in her lap. She regarded me suspiciously.

"How can I get out to Bala-Bala?" she asked.

"It's not easy; not many schooners go out there."

"Mr Elkington said you would be going back to Ysabel tomorrow."

"Yes, but only to Tataba. Bala-Bala is miles farther on up the coast.

"Will you take me as far as Tataba?"

"No, that's impossible."

"Why? I'm willing to pay."

"There's no question of payment."

"Well, what's your objection?"

I recoiled instinctively from having any part in her going out to Bala-Bala.

"The *Wai-ai's* not suitable for women passengers," I said. "I couldn't possibly take you out in her."

She blushed slightly, but was not diverted from her object by notions of delicacy. She went on stubbornly.

"White women travel in these ships, don't they?"

"Oh yes, people who have lived in the Islands."

"Well, if they can manage, I can."

She took a handkerchief from her bag and mopped her brow. She scowled and her face darkened as she waited for me to speak.

"That's not all. You might be a couple of weeks or more at Tataba with me before you could get to Bala-Bala."

She fumbled with her bag impatiently.

"Oh, for goodness' sake, would that worry you?"

"It wouldn't worry me, but it would be impossible for you."

She made a brusque gesture.

"Listen, mister," she said leaning, towards me. "What do you think I am? You won't hurt me, and nobody would care anyway. What time do you leave tomorrow?"

"I am not taking you to Ysabel, Mrs Cullen; that's definite." I stood up. "Please excuse me."

She put out her hand as though to detain me.

"Please take me," she implored.

I moved away, but she followed me. Distress made her ugly and I looked at her with distaste. I turned my back on her and hastened towards the bar. She stood, undecided on the verandah, and then walked slowly to her room.

There were now four people in the bar. Tom gave me a keen look when I joined them. I was about to protest at his suggesting that I might take the woman to Bala-Bala, but changed my mind. He probably thought I ought to, and when he found that I had refused he was likely to turn on me with a quick spurt of temper and express his disapproval.

I left after lunch and spent the night anchored at Buena Vista. I reached Tataba at ten o'clock in the morning.

I had been back two days. It was the end of the month and I had spent the afternoon trying to balance the cash book. Hoile had a bad septic sore on his leg and I had let him go off for the day. I was startled when someone suddenly said, "Halloey." I looked up at the door and saw the sly good-humoured features of Paley. I had not seen him since I fined him for illegal dynamiting.

"Hullo, Paley, you blackguard; I didn't hear the *Daphne* come in," I said. "What have you been up to lately?"

He came slowly across the room and sat in the chair facing me. He wiped his brow with a sweat-towel and laughed.

"Have a heart, Mr Fowler. Let bygones be bygones," he pleaded with an air of candour. "It's a stinker today all right, isn't it?"

He took out a tin of cigarettes from his pocket and offered me one.

214

"Will you have a cigarette?"

"No, thank you," I said.

"Do you mind if I smoke?" he enquired courteously, with an ingratiating smile.

"Come off it, Paley, what is it you want?"

"Well, as a matter of fact I've run out of drinking water. I was wondering if you could let me have three or four tins."

"Where have you come from?"

"Tulagi."

"You've come from Tulagi, and I suppose you forgot to fill up before you left. What sort of schooner captain do you call yourself?"

"That's where you're wrong. I did fill up, but I've got a passenger who does a lot of drinking and washing."

"You've got a passenger in the *Daphne*?" I said. "Where's he for?"

He flicked ash off his cigarette and spoke nonchalantly.

"For Bala-Bala."

My heart sank; I looked at Paley sharply.

"For Bala-Bala? you haven't by any chance got an unfortunate woman called Cullen on board?"

Paley smiled, but there was mockery in his eyes.

"Why yes, Mr Fowler, I'm taking Peter Cullen's missus to Bala-Bala."

I was tempted to hit him. Maybe I was concerned less with the feelings of the woman than with fear of trouble for myself.

"You are a swine, Paley," I said.

Paley pretended to be indignant. "That remark was uncalled for," he said. "I take serious exception to it."

"You know Cullen keeps a couple of native women going and gets stinking drunk for a week at a time. Nobody but a swine would take a white woman to that set-up."

Paley shrugged his shoulders. "I'm just a trader and recruiter trying to make a living," he said with mock humility. "Maybe that's why I just can't see what Peter Cullen and his wife have got to do with you."

I found it hard to keep my temper.

"I believe you are doing this just to make trouble for me," I said.

The shadow of a smile hovered round Paley's lips. He took another cigarette from the tin and lit it.

"You get the strangest ideas about me. I'm taking Mrs Cullen for a cash payment of twenty pounds—anyway, she's entitled to join her husband.

"Take your three tins of water," I told him. "You can tell the woman she can rest and clean herself up at the house. Now get out of this office."

"I'll send up for the water, but I'm afraid Mrs Cullen won't accept any favours from you. She doesn't like you."

"She can please herself."

Paley stood up to go. "Why is it I always seem to get on the wrong side of you?" he asked.

"Skip it," I told him curtly.

"We must have a drink together some day."

He raised his right hand in a half salute. As he went out he smiled knowingly, as though we shared a secret or were party to a conspiracy of some sort.

I thought of Mrs Cullen for the rest of the afternoon.

The *Daphne* was dirty and small. A cabin amidships was used as a trade store and labour recruits or labourers being returned to their homes were apt to crowd the remaining space in the ship. After tea I walked down to the wharf and went off to the *Daphne*. Mrs Cullen looked startled when I went alongside and called out her name. She had no shoes on and her hair was untidy. She was blowsy with heat and discomfort.

"Mr Paley's not here," she said.

"I've come down to see you, Mrs Cullen."

She looked at me suspiciously. I had seldom met anyone with so little feminine charm.

"What d'you want?"

"I'm sorry you've decided to come out here. I certainly can't stop you. It won't be very comfortable here tonight, but won't you come up to the house for a meal and, if you like, sleep ashore?"

216

She was sitting in a grubby canvas chair on a patch of dirty deck aft. A labourer pushed his way between us as we talked. There was misery in her face and for a moment I thought she was yielding to the temptation of accepting my invitation. Then her face hardened and she glowered at me.

"No, thank you, Mr Fowler," she said. "I wouldn't care to be beholden to you. I've put up with this so far and I'll put up with it as far as Bala-Bala. I could have done with your help in Tulagi, but you refused it. Please don't worry about me."

It would have been useless to argue with her; she looked an unintelligent and stubborn woman.

"You must please yourself," I said. "If you change your mind, you will be welcome."

She turned away as though my presence was offensive to her. I left her and met Paley as I walked along the wharf on my way back to the house.

"Hullo, hullo," he greeted me roguishly. "Have you been visiting my passenger? Don't be put off by appearances; many a sweet tune's been played on an old fiddle."

"You are a disgusting little beast, Paley."

He laughed and went on to the end of the wharf and called for the boat.

Next morning when I looked out about six o'clock I saw that the *Daphne* had gone.

I finished the month-end work and then went away for five days. I spent the last night at Kesuo Cove, where the Spanish navigator Mendaña had made his base. There had been no break in the weather—hour after hour the engine drove the *Wai-ai* through a glassy, almost unmoving sea. We had been four hours on an east-south-east course passing reefs, islets and shoal patches down the north-west coast of the island. I hoped to reach Tataba before nightfall. My eyes ached from much reading and I had become stiff from sitting too long. I got up and went for'ard. For a time I looked down at the water dis-coloured by inky clouds where an octopus had been alarmed, or at the porpoises, keeping just ahead, plunging and curvetting and occasionally cleaving the surface of the water with a fin.

H   217

Then I returned to my chair, to read and doze, wearied by the thought of the long journey before me.

Hoile coughed behind my back.

"What's the matter with you?" I demanded.

"I think somebody wants us."

"Where?"

He gazed out from the starboard side.

"See that canoe?" he said.

I got up again and joined him. There was a small wooded island off the shore at the end of a massive reef. If Hoile had not pointed, I would not have seen the canoe against the trees. There was only one man in it and he was holding up a paddle.

"We'll go in," I said.

The *Wai-ai* came round. Hoile went for'ard and joined in shouted conversation across the water with the man in the canoe.

"A white woman at Bala-Bala wants you," he said. "I think Peter Cullen's wife."

The presentiment I had felt about the woman had been well founded. Anything might have happened. We were about four miles off the coast. It would take us nearly an hour to get to the anchorage. I grudged the time we should lose, but I would have to go in to see what she wanted.

For such a still day the sea was breaking heavily on the barrier reef. We went through the passage and then between two islands and then on at half speed among coral heads to the anchorage in front of the copra shed. There was no one on the beach, but as I went ashore in the boat the woman came out of the house. I met her on the path. She was carrying two fibre suit-cases; in a strap round one there was a short-handled umbrella and a rain-coat.

"I'll go back for the hat-box," she said.

"Where's Peter, does he know you're leaving?" I asked.

"I don't know where he is—I haven't seen him for four days.

"I'll get the hat-box. Go aboard the *Wai-ai*."

She picked up the cases like a woman accustomed to helping herself.

218

"Leave them," I told her. "The boys will take care of those."

Wesu and Gagi pulled the dinghy up on to dry shingle and I helped her to get into it. I watched them push off and row out. Then I walked up to the house. There was no sign of Cullen there. I went down rickety back steps and along to the labourers' houses. A naked child screamed and ran to its mother, the boss-boy's wife, a big woman with large pendulous breasts who was pounding taro. She spoke harshly to the child and shook it. There was nobody else there.

"Where's Peter?" I asked.

She put down the wooden pestle and turned with a grimace towards the village.

"He's at Koseo."

"What, he sleep there?"

"Yes, he get drunk too much; woman belong him come take him. He sleep for house belong her."

The village was three miles away. It was unlikely that I would get any sense from Cullen if I went there.

"Tell him I take white woman back to Tulagi," I said.

She pursed her lips and took up the pestle again.

"More better you do alla same. Peter no good for white woman."

She began pounding taro again. The child stared at me open eyed, no longer afraid. I went to the house for the hat-box.

Mrs Cullen thanked me when I rejoined her, but said nothing else. She aroused no personal feelings in me; there was nothing about her to excite compassion. I told her I would get her to Tulagi in time for the mail-boat. I made no attempt at conversation above the noise of the engine. After lunch I asked her to take the deck-chair or my bunk. "Sleep is the only way to pass time," I said. She did not want to sleep, and chose to sit in the deck-chair.

Beni brewed tea about five o'clock and I told him to open a tin of biscuits. The woman accepted what I offered with thanks, but she was preoccupied and had apparently no more wish to talk than I had. We reached Tataba at a quarter to seven. "I'll send the *Wai-ai* with you to Tulagi tomorrow," I said. She made no reply, but pointed at the suit-case she wanted and walked in silence with me up the hill.

She changed the brown dress for one with a flowered pattern, made her hair tidy and powdered her face. She took off the walking-shoes and put on sandals. We sat near the windows in the sitting-room. She refused a cigarette, but accepted whisky. I smoked and drank waiting for food. She stared through the open window at the warm humid darkness outside, listless and inattentive. I looked at her occasionally and made an attempt at conversation, but got no reply. I went to the kitchen and told Beni to hurry up with the food. When I sat down again at the window, the woman turned and looked at me.

"I'm being a nuisance to you," she said.

"No," I said. "The *Wai-ai* has to go for stores sometime; she can go tomorrow and take you."

She turned away again and stared through the window and then started speaking slowly and weakly, as though she was thinking out loud.

"I know now why you didn't want to bring me to Bala-Bala," she said.

The lamp was smoking. I got up and turned down the wick.

"You haven't got to talk about it," I said.

She sipped the drink and then put down the glass on the stool near her chair. She continued to stare out at the night, but started talking again.

"I'm a sister at Wallamarra General Hospital. I was on duty one night four years ago when the police brought Peter into Casualty. He was in a terrible mess. He had been picked up in the road with a broken leg and cuts and bruises and he'd got D.T.'s."

She droned on tonelessly with no expression in her voice. I poured out more whisky for her. She made a half-hearted gesture of refusal, but then accepted it.

"He was in hospital for three months. I saw him in the ward every day. After the first week I thought he was quite a decent bloke. When he was discharged he took me out when I was off duty. One day someone came to the place where I lived and warned me against him. He said he was a terrible drinker and had a native woman in the Islands. I told him to mind his own business. I didn't love Peter, but I was thirty-seven and I liked him well enough. We got married. I stopped work and we took a furnished flat in Elizabeth Bay. The English cricketers were in Australia; we went every day to the Test Match and spent a lot of time on the beaches. Peter had plenty of money and we had a wonderful time for three months. One morning he went to the bank and didn't come home. Next day a policeman came to the flat to say he was locked up in a cell. He had met someone down town and had got drunk. He had broken a plate-glass window in George Street and had fought with the police. He was lucky to get away with a fine. I don't want to bore you with all this. Peter was drunk nearly all the time after that and was always in trouble. I left him and went back to work. I saw him again before he left. He was quite sober and we had supper at the Australia. He asked me to go back with him to the Solomons. I didn't trust him; he begged me to but I was afraid. I told him to ask me after he had been back six months and I would think about it."

"Did he write?"

"No, and I sent him small presents at Christmas, but he never acknowledged them. I worried a lot about the whole thing and thought I might be wrong somehow."

The nine o'clock drum sounded and Beni announced that the food was on the table. We stood up and went to the dining-room.

After supper she walked out on the front verandah. Moon-light lay over the station and someone on the wharf was pluck-ing a steel-stringed guitar.

"It's lovely here," she said. "I thought Bala-Bala would be something like this." She laughed bitterly.

"What was it like there?" I said.

We went back to the chairs in the sitting-room. She sat in silence as though reflecting, and then shrugged her fleshy shoulders. She turned towards me with a glowering sulky expression. "If anyone's entitled to know, you are," she said.

Atiu interrupted us with coffee, and then came back with brandy. I rarely drank it, but I poured out two glasses and he took one and placed it next to Mrs Cullen's coffee on the stool at her side. She looked at it doubtfully, but said nothing.

"For a couple of days Peter was quite decent. He didn't say why he hadn't answered my letters, and I didn't ask him. I was beginning to think I might make a go of it, although it was very rough there. Then awful things began to happen at night."

She faced me again. "You know the house, of course?"

"Yes."

"You know the orange trees at the back?"

"Yes, they are all useless. The fruit has got no juice—there's nothing but hard dry pith in them."

"That's right; they are like cricket balls. There were a lot of them lying about on the ground under the trees. About nine o'clock some devil started throwing these oranges on to the corrugated iron roof. That more than anything nearly drove me mad. It's deathly quiet there at night and then suddenly these things used to hit the iron and clatter down the roof to the ground. Sometimes there would be silence for half an hour and just when we thought we were going to have some peace it would start again and there would be three in five minutes. It went on all night and it was impossible to sleep. I used to think of some creature in the darkness choosing her time to toss those things on to the iron."

"Peter said he didn't know who was doing it but the small boy in the house told me it was a woman from the village. Peter knew all right. Then he started to drink. I didn't know there was whisky in the stores that Paley brought. Peter was drunk for three days, then he wandered off and I didn't see him again. The boy said he was living in his woman's house in the village." She laughed sardonically. "Anyway, there were no more oranges on the roof after that."

She fell silent and then went on. "I don't know what would

have happened if you hadn't come along. It was the boy's idea to look out for you; I'd never have thought of it."

I walked down to the wharf with her next morning. There was a buoyancy in her manner which I had not seen before. She chattered brightly all the way down the hill.

"Give me a ring when you are in Sydney," she said, "and we might have tea somewhere."

She handed me a scrap of paper with her name, address and telephone number on it. I thanked her and said I would remember her invitation.

There was an awkward silence on the wharf as we reached the *Wai-ai*.

"I'm very sorry you've had such a dreadful experience out here," I said. "I'd have prevented it if I could. I blame that little swine Paley more than anyone."

She looked at me in surprise. "Don't be sorry for me," she exclaimed, "and don't blame Mr Paley for anything. This trip has been just what the doctor ordered for me. Dinkum, it's the best thing that has ever happened to me. I've had such a bellyful of Peter and the Solomon Islands I never want to hear them mentioned again. I've got Peter right out of my system— I'm going back to Sydney now and I'll never give him another thought. Honestly, I feel as though a heavy load's been taken off me; I really do feel fine."

There was such honesty and spontaneity in her declaration that I laughed out loud.

"Peter's been niggling at me all these years, but not any more. Never again."

She peered into the *Wai-ai* to make sure her baggage was on board and then turned and gave me a firm hand-clasp.

"See you in Sydney," she said and then stepped awkwardly aboard.

I stood on the wharf until the *Wai-ai* was under way. I waved at her once and then went up the hill to the office. It was not Paley's fault things had turned out the way they had. I would have something to say to him when I next saw him.

CHAPTER TEN

The End

FROM the waterfront I could have gone through the cutting to the hospital—it was nearer that way—but I chose to walk round the headland past the barbed-wire fence of the gaol. Coral-gravel paths, bordered with trimmed lime-stone and clipped bushes, led to hospital buildings which were sheltered from the sun by cultivated trees and bushes. It was ten o'clock when I stood outside the doctor's room. A light-skinned Polynesian girl, taller and slimmer than the Melanesians of the Solomons, came out and walked barefoot along the verandah. A hibiscus bloom was stuck in her long straight hair; her closely wrapped cloth had a gay floral pattern. Crichton had his head over his desk writing when I went in.

"What's the matter with her?" I asked.

"Who?"

I nodded down the verandah. "The dusky beauty."

"Mind your own business." He demanded caustically, "What's wrong with you?"

"I've got some boils, and I feel part worn," I said.

"Take your shirt off and lie on the couch," he ordered.

He was a long time examining me. He sounded my back and chest with what seemed excessive care.

"When are you due for leave?" he asked.

"I've got another six months to do."

"It's too long."

"Don't tell me that."

"I can give you a tonic, but it won't help much. We'll get those boils dressed and I'll give you an injection. Get a supply

225

of Marmite and those sores on your mouth will clear up."

"What's this skin condition I've got on my ribs and right shoulder?"

"*Tinea circanta tropica* we call it; the native name is *bakua*. It's a form of ringworm. I could give you something to clear it up, but you'd get it again."

"Why should I?"

"You spend your life in the *Wai-ai* with crew, police, prisoners and sick people all round you?"

"Yes, we are often a bit cramped."

"I'll give you some ointment when you go on leave. It will go in a few days when you get out of the tropics."

A hospital orderly in a white *lava lava* dressed the boils on my buttocks.

"That better?" Crichton asked.

"Yes," I said.

He regarded me thoughtfully.

"How's your weight?"

"I reckon I've lost a bit."

"Yes," he said slowly. "I really ought to admit you."

"Why?"

He seemed at a loss for words and spoke as though he did not wish to alarm me.

"There's an abnormality in your chest which should be investigated—it's probably nothing at all but . . ."

I interrupted him.

"You mean I might have lung trouble—T.B.?"

"Well, yes," he agreed. "That's the extreme possibility."

I laughed. "You cough and spit with T.B.?"

"Maybe, but there's a rale in your left lung; it's probably nothing, but I can't tell until I've had a proper look at you."

"I must get back to Tataba; I can't come into hospital now."

"All right," he said reluctantly, "but see me in a month's time, and in the meantime take care of yourself. When you go on leave I'll give you a letter to someone in Sydney. You ought to be screened."

The End

The head-rope and the stern-rope were made fast and the *Wai-ai* hove in broadside to the wharf. Hiro met me when I stepped ashore.

"Walter Notere come?" I asked him at once.

After my return from Tulagi I had gone a hundred and fifty miles, as far as Kia at the north end of the island, collecting taxes. For three days and nights in Maringe Lagoon I had sat in the *Wai-ai* writing receipts, sometimes by lamp-light, until two or three in the morning with the deck littered with the scraps of paper and cloth, creased brown leaves, lengths of fibre and bits of fish twine with which coin had been packed. Some people had come a long distance to pay, and those from bush villages had travelled hard. Whenever people arrived—night or day—I attended to them in the *Wai-ai*.

From Maringe Lagoon to Kia we sailed before the south-east trade and I was burned and fatigued by the sun. When we returned down the coast, the sea got up and the *Wai-ai*, pitching and shipping sea, made poor time. I stepped ashore at Tataba wet and tired, and my arms and face had begun to peel.

"Walter Notere come?" I asked Hiro again.

"He's not come," he replied.

I was angry. I had not seen Notere since I returned from Tulagi. He had done nothing to help with tax-collection.

"Why has he not come?" I demanded.

"He's sick."

"Sick? Who says he's sick?"

"Constable Busa has been to Furona to tell Walter to come here. He saw Walter in bed; he's very sick and will soon die."

Hoile and Wetera carried the strong box to the office. It was heavy, with three hundred pounds in coin. The prisoners arranged my baggage on the wharf to carry to the house.

"Leave it," I told the warder.

He looked at me in surprise.

"Leave it," I repeated wearily. "Leave it."

I worked by lamp-light in the office—there was a lot to do after my tour—and when I walked along the wharf in the

227

This Island's Mine

morning Palukue was waiting there with three other men from Regi. I said that they could come. Hiro's box was on the deck for'ard. "I'd like to come," he said.

The wind had dropped, but there was still a head sea and the ship pitched with clockwork regularity all the way along the coast to Cape Prieto. We anchored for the night at Vulavu. The headman came off as soon as the cable ran out and asked if he and some of his people could join us.

More people came during the night; people from villages we had passed up the coast crowded into the *Wai-ai* until there was no room to move. We left at dawn. Off Laluala a canoe intercepted us. "No more people on board," I told Soge. "Tell them we'll tow them." As we entered Thousand Ships Bay another canoe came out and there was a third from Kaevaga. At our normal speed of six knots the canoes, yawing from side to side from tow ropes, were drawn back on the course with abrupt dangerous strains and we were compelled to reduce speed. We went slowly up the dreary coast to Furona. I sat surrounded and pressed in by patient impassive-looking natives, an actor in events moving to a climax. The news had spread widely that Notere was dying.

We cast off the canoes at the passage and went through the reef to the anchorage. Notere's brother came to meet me at the beach. Tears poured down his chubby face when I asked for news. "Belly belong him sore too much," he said. "He no savvy *kai kai*; he t'row out everyt'ing."

Furona was crowded. We walked through the silent curious crowd to Walter's house. It was built of native materials five feet off the ground on piles and was designed a little like a white man's house, with five rooms and a wide verandah. Outside the house, at one end, six sheets of corrugated iron were fitted over a framework and a length of guttering carried rain water away to a tank. I saw Walter's wife at the house. She was twenty-five years younger than he. She wore a short smock-like garment with ruffled shoulders to cover her bosom; there were strips of coloured braid sewn round the bottom of her cloth. She had anklets of threaded porpoise teeth. Notere lay on

228

a bed in the main room. He had been washed and his clothing and blankets were tidy. But I was shocked by his appearance; he was emaciated, shrunken and very old looking. I found it difficult to speak with composure. I touched him gently and told him to lie down when he greeted me in a whisper and tried to sit up.

There was nothing I could do for him. The people round him were more competent than I was. They fed him on coconut milk in a small shell. Once, when they gave him pounded yam, he vomited immediately. He was starving to death, I thought.

Notere was sinking when I saw him next morning. His brother and four other men of the family were in the room with him. His wife and another woman were preparing a shroud from tapa cloth in the adjoining room. People of less importance waited on the verandah and in other rooms. Outside the crowd, subdued with the patient expectation of death, talked quietly or stood in silence. The child of Notere's old age, an unpleasant boy of seven, ran about outside with other children, flaunting his right to enter the house where the others dared not follow.

Notere died at four o'clock in the afternoon. He lay serene and dignified as his brother, standing with me, looked at him and wept without restraint. The people in the crowd outside chattered freely as I walked among them returning with Hiro to the *Wai-ai*. I started at the sight of a man in a group on the fringe of the crowd. I looked back at him puzzled. He could not be the man he appeared to me because, as I told myself, that would be impossible.

We left the crowd and took a sandy path through a coconut grove to the boat landing place. The notion persisted, but it was so fantastic that I hesitated to mention it.

"I thought I saw Hamutagi," I said at last to Hiro.

"He's here; he came about midnight."

"Hamutagi?" I queried with disbelief.

"Yes, he's here," Hiro asserted again. "We saw him arrive."

Hamutagi was the priest of the mission, an enemy of

Notere's who time and again had accused him of all manner of evil. He was one of the old *vunagi kiloau*, men of the church, resentful and brooding, who looked on me with suspicion and dislike. He could not be at Furona for any good purpose. Indeed, his appearance there at that time offended me.

"What does he want here at this time?" I asked crossly. "Didn't he know Walter was dying?"

"He wanted to see Walter before he died; he talked to him last night. He's waiting now until they bury him."

I was sceptical.

"This man has said a lot of bad things about Walter, and everybody knows it."

I protested so vehemently that Hiro was silenced. He pushed off the boat with Gagi and Wesu; as he stepped aboard the edge of his *lava lava* touched the water. I said nothing until we were almost alongside. Hiro squeezed out water from his *lava lava*. I asked him again about Hamutagi and Notere.

"Didn't you know that Walter had joined the mission?" Hiro said.

I looked at him with derision and called him aft when he got on board.

"Walter join mission, you say? What nonsense. Mission has always said Walter was like the devil."

Hiro spoke patiently. "While you were at Tulagi, all the mission leaders asked Walter to join the Church. I thought you knew."

"I did not know. Did Walter join the Church?"

"Yes, he did."

I told Hiro he could go. If what he said was true, and it must be true, it was fantastic—so fantastically good that I feared evil concealed somewhere or yet to emerge.

Someone banged the board on the edge of my bunk. It was half-past four. I turned my torch towards the thermometer hanging on the bulkhead near the clock. It registered seventy-three degrees, a summer temperature at home but chilly for us as I stood in pyjamas wondering what was wrong. I went up

230

on deck. The riding light on the forestay had burned out, but I recognised Hiro's outline in the gloom.

"What's the matter?" I asked.

"They are going to bury Walter," he said.

I was hardly awake, and my mind worked slowly.

"Bury him now, a big man like Walter? Why don't they leave him two or three days so that everyone can come and see him?"

"His brother does not agree; he wants him buried now."

"Wait," I said.

We carried a lamp through the grove and along the path to the village. We passed a heap of fresh earth; the ground had been opened during the night. The crowd made way and I mounted the steps to the house with Hiro behind me. I started when I saw the shrouded body, lashed in a crouching position, obscured by blue-dyed tapa cloth and propped up on the bed. The form was that of a living person, bound and suffocating, but the smell of death was in the room. Nobody spoke, but there must have been a sign, for Hiro said in a low voice, "Everyone's ready to go now."

In the first light of dawn six men carried Notere's body on a litter to the ground which had been prepared for it beyond the coconut grove where there had once been a garden. The men put down the litter and three of them lifted the body vertically and lowered it into the hole. Hamutagi read from a book in the light of a lamp, but the crowd which followed stared without heeding while Notere's brother put the belt and red sash with the body and others of the family filled up the grave with coral stones and earth.

It took us two days to travel back the hundred and ten miles to Tataba. We tied up at sunset on the second day and Hoile met me at the wharf.

"Paley came in the *Daphne* yesterday," he reported. "He said he wanted to see you. I said you were not here."

"Where did he go?" I asked.

"He went back to Tulagi."

I was glad I had missed Paley.

"He bring mail?"

"There's a small packet of mail at the house."

I sauntered up the hill. No overseas mail was due and I was in no hurry. In fact, I found only three local letters in the sealed and labelled mail-bag. The one addressed in Darcy's handwriting was the only important one. My heart fluttered as I read it. Crichton had been to see him about me and on his advice Darcy had decided that I must go on leave as soon as possible. John Priestly would come out in three weeks' time to take over from me.

So I was to go on leave in three weeks' time, two and a half months before I had expected to do so. Quite suddenly the pleasure this news gave to me turned to dust and ashes. There was nothing wrong with me; I could finish my tour; there was no difference really between thirty-four months and thirty-six months. Moreover, there were developments in the island which only I could understand. A change at Tataba now might be disastrous.

As I lay awake that night I became more certain of the folly of Darcy's proposal. I lit a lamp and strode up and down the verandah smoking incessantly; and then I sat down and wrote and destroyed three different letters protesting against my early departure. I fell asleep just before dawn and was roused at daylight by Beni shaking the bed. I went to the office dispirited and tired and wrote to Darcy saying that I looked forward to seeing John Priestly.

When Hiro reported that morning, I told him the news.

"In three weeks, I go," I said.

His usual formal manner failed him; his mouth fell open and he looked at me keenly with surprise.

"In three weeks you go?" he asked.

"Yes."

"Who's coming here?"

"Mr Priestly."

"Mr Priestly, I know him, he's a good man."

He stood staring at me speculatively until I dismissed him.

He paused at Hoile's table and there was whispered conversation.

I had finished touring the district and my next journey would be to Tulagi to go home. I was left with a few days to write notes for Priestly.

I had been two days at the work. I fell into a state of abstraction as I tried to describe the district and its problems. Hiro came to the office in the middle of the morning and stood awkwardly before me. He cleared his throat.

"We hear many people will come to see you tomorrow," he said.

Priestly was due in four days time; I wanted nothing to complicate my handing over to him.

"Where did you hear this?" I asked warily.

"They are saying it in Regi."

I felt a quick rise of temper and spoke irritably.

"Don't you know I've been in this place nearly three years? If anyone wants to see me, he can see me and I'll hear what he has to say."

"I know," he said without moving.

"All right then," I said. "Don't interrupt me again with this kind of talk."

Hiro went out.

During the afternoon Hoile came into the room. "There's a big canoe coming," he said.

I got up and gazed out from the doorway. Snowy cumulus clouds piled high against the bright blue sky; tiny white caps whipped up by the light south-east trade wind speckled the blue sea as far as the horizon. It was a mild balmy day, the beginning of the south-east season. Just beyond the pin rocks eastward of Martin Point a very big canoe, it looked like a *biabina*, biggest of Bugotu canoes, was heading for Tataba. There were thirty or more paddlers, and as they paddled they struck the gunwale of the canoe with paddle shafts in unison. The rhythmic sound came echoing over the water as the canoe drew nearer and nearer. Now paddled slower, she approached the beach and I could see the line of white cowries sweeping

233

up to the figure at the top of the prow and downwards towards the water line to the *muju*, the grotesque-faced figure-head. The paddlers were now walking the canoe through shallow water towards the sand; they would soon beach her. Hoile stood ten paces away from me on the right; he suddenly exclaimed "Koi!" He shouted with unsuppressed excitement. "Look, master, look; two more *biabina!*"

Coming round the rocks in line were two more *biabina*. Already I could hear the rap of paddles and the swishing sound as the paddles scooped up water, propelling the big canoes towards the beach. I was thrilled by the spectacle of these majestic craft, now moving abreast with a swirl of water, coming steadily nearer. Then with excited shouts the paddlers shortened their strokes and, striking more rapidly, began to race. The canoes shot forward out of a mist of spray and exultant cries reached me. Then prudence intervened, the momentum of the canoes was checked, and they came slowly through the passage in the reef.

That afternoon more canoes appeared round Martin Point and others came down the coast across Fulakora Bay. Towards evening they came in a stream converging on Regi and Tataba.

At night, as I sat at the house after supper, shrieks pierced the darkness and sounds of unusual gaiety came up from the beach. The constable who drummed at nine o'clock went on beating the hollow log with light-hearted freedom going on unceasing until it was time for him to sound ten o'clock.

Before he left the house Beni brought me the cocoa I had taken to drinking at night. As he put the mug on the stool near my chair there were loud shouts from the beach and bursts of uproarious laughter. Beni stared out into the darkness and then turned to me with shining eyes. "Many people come to play at Tataba," he said with wonderment in his voice.

"Yes," I answered and drank the cocoa.

He took the empty mug and went out slowly, his head half turned to the open window to catch the sounds from the beach.

Hiro's cryptic allusion had not prepared me for what I saw

next morning. The parade ground, the paths and the beach
were thronged by the biggest crowd I had seen at Tataba. Men
for the most part, but women and children too, wandered
about as though with no purpose. Someone would tell me, I
supposed, why they had come.

To kill time I sat at the table and read through the notes I
had written. Then Hiro marched in, right turned to face me,
and saluted. "It's time for you to come now," he said, "everything is ready." I got up in silence and followed him down the
path to the beach. The crowd was now ranged round the edge
of the parade ground. Hamutagi was in the centre, standing,
book in hand with three deacons. Twenty-five men and
youths, some wearing trade singlets with their *lava lavas*,
and fifteen women, bare bosomed, three or four with infants,
formed a choir. There were hymns, readings, prayers, more
hymns and then the benediction. I was profoundly moved by
the simple service, the more so, perhaps, because I was unprepared for it. As soon as it was over I walked out quickly
to intercept Hamutagi before he left. My first impulse was to
embrace him, but I restrained myself and merely took his
hand when I thanked him. He seemed shy with me at first,
but when I added that I hoped I would soon see him again,
he paused for a moment, nodded and smiled, and then walked
on.

Twenty men were out in the field as soon as the clergy and
choir had moved off. Each man's hair was limed; they had tied
white cloths about their heads and their bodies were draped with
pandanus leaf. Leaning slightly forward the men advanced
with a shout, stamping and prancing on the hard ground; they
came forward and retired again and again until, breathless and
sweating, they disappeared into the crowd. Women now took
the field, twelve of them adorned with clam shell arm-rings
and porpoise-teeth necklaces; around their ankles dried seed-
pods threaded on fibre rustled and clattered rhythmically as
they stamped out the dance. More men came out dancing at
high speed with their heads crowned with the greenery of
coconut fronds. Women followed carrying decorated bamboo

235

poles with white cock feathers bunched at the top. Men sat on the ground in a row, twisting, turning and bending to the clap of hands, going through the motions of traditional rites until the sound of high-pitched whoops drew attention away from them. Men, their bodies painted and carrying shields and clubs, rushed out in a war dance. They gyrated and shrieked in belligerent display and then went off at the end of the field. At first no one followed, but then two men, one tall and the other short and slim, danced out to the centre of the field—the tall man raising and lowering his arms, his body swaying, moved forward; the smaller man with similar motions darted from right to left and moved backwards to avoid the other. So they went round the field, the tall man drawing closer and closer until the short man, turning his head from side to side as though seeking escape, abandoned flight and shielding his face with his hands sank cowering on to the ground and the tall man, with outstretched hands, threw himself upon him.

The crowd, now tired of dancing, swarmed over the open field. On the far side of the barrack there were preparations for feasting. Portions of food on leaves lay in a line a hundred yards long. The milk and scrapings of coconuts had been added to pounded yam. There were puddings of taro, banana and *nali* nuts pounded together. Boiled taro in loosely plaited baskets was there by the ton, and I had never before seen so many bonito fish. Palukue joined me as I stared at the food.

"This is a wonderful feast," I said.

"Yes," he said with obvious pleasure. "The mission women have done well."

There were lumps of greasy meat on the leaves.

"Have you killed a pig?" I asked.

"Oh yes, the hunters killed three large pigs."

I called Hiro. "Issue two bags of rice," I told him.

The crowd moved and ranged itself along the line of food. Palukue and two other elders, Fafi and Hage from villages up the coast, were in charge. The crowd waited for a sign. Hamutagi said a grace, and then they reached for the food and began to eat. I found myself alone; there was no place for me there. For fifteen minutes I looked on at the feasting and then, uncertain of what was expected of me, I walked away across the deserted parade ground to the beach. Canoes, pulled up on the sand by the score lay there, gunwales almost touching. A few people who had not waited for the feast were beginning to leave.

Priestly came in the *Hygeia*. For three nights we talked until midnight. On the fourth morning he said he was ready to take over and I told Soge to be ready to leave with me at ten o'clock that night for Tulagi.

Hiro and all the police, Joe with his wife standing a little apart, the warder, the two long-sentence prisoners who so often had carried my baggage, Palukue, Raji, and two other men from Regi were at the end of the wharf when Priestly walked down with me to the *Wai-ai*. I shook each of them by the hand and made some sort of remark. I stepped aboard and Soge started the engine and gave orders to cast off.

The moon was in its first quarter and shed a poor cheerless light through an overcast sky. It was chilly on deck and I went below for a jacket. When I looked back at the wharf Priestly was walking away behind a flickering ellipse of light where his torch threw its beam on the ground. The police and the other people remained standing in a dark huddled mass where I had left them. We made the serpentine sweep round the reefs and got on our course for Tulagi and I could now only see the yellow glimmer of the hurricane lamp at the end of the wharf. Then, like the rise of a great orange moon, a sudden glow on the rocky tip of Martin Point sent a wide swathe of reflected red light over the water. Before I had recovered from this dramatic happening, long tongues of yellow red flame shot upwards into the sky and the rocks and trees at the end of the point appeared as clearly as by day. I stood for'ard of the mast, gripping the main shrouds on the starboard side. The fire, growing bigger and bigger, sent a ruddy glow high into the sky and made a roaring and crackling that was audible half a mile away above the noise of the engine. I stood for a long time staring past the point until we were passing between the islands and the mainland approaching Cape Prieto and heading for the open sea beyond. I could no longer see the fire, but the glow in the sky remained. I went to my bunk feeling sad and bereaved and more tired than I even remembered feeling before. I fell asleep at once.

When I awoke we were off Gela and it was daylight. Warm rain fell with a steady dull insistence. It dripped from the awning and made the ship damp and uncomfortable. The rain stopped before we reached the islands off Tulagi, the sun shone and the wind freshened from the south-east. We tied up at Government Wharf just before noon. The *Mataram* lay at Makambo across the harbour loading copra. In two days time I would embark in her on the first stage of my journey home.

"Tell the crew to come," I said to Soge.

The three men joined him and looked at me blankly. I stood up, stirred by emotion, but with no coherent thoughts in my mind.

"For three years you have manned the *Wai-ai* and we have travelled many many miles together," I said. "In two days I go aboard the steamer for Sydney, and there I go aboard another steamer for England."

I looked at each man in turn. Soge displayed polite interest, but each of the other three looked back at me wonderingly.

"I want to thank you for the good work you have done for me."

Soge listened attentively. His intelligent face lit up and he smiled attractively. Almost immediately Wesu spoke.

"Yes?" I said. "Wesu wants to say something?"

Soge became impersonal again.

"Wesu say more better me fella dry sail now."

I stepped down to the wharf. Darcy's orderly, twenty yards away, came towards me with a letter. In the *Wai-ai* there was a squeak of blocks as they hauled down on the halyards raising the mainsail. It would soon dry in the warm sun and fresh breeze.

Postscript

IN 1942 the Japanese invaded the Solomons. The Resident Commissioner moved his headquarters from Tulagi to Auki on Malaita. Administrative officers remained on duty, boldly maintained British administration of the islands, and faithfully discharged many new duties which war, with the enemy in their midst, brought to them. They could have done nothing, they would have been lost, without the loyal cooperation of Solomon Islanders who had learned to trust their white men.

A small flotilla of schooners was assembled in the Western Solomons and performed many tasks. Indentured labourers, stranded by the tide of war, were taken back to their homes, supplies were carried to refugee camps, and communications were kept going with even the most remote and isolated places. When the Japanese came in greater strength and established outposts, the schooners were employed in more offensive action. Men were embarked and taken through enemy lines and disembarked after dark in waters which the enemy supposed himself to be in control. These men then moved silently up to the enemy outposts, destroyed the garrisons, re-embarked and returned in the schooner which had brought them. The finest ship of them all was the *Wai-ai*, a gaff sloop, forty feet long and thirteen in the beam and with a high mast. She had been built in a Sydney shipyard for ocean racing. Her first owner raced her in the Tasman Sea. Her mast was shortened and her sail area reduced, an engine was installed and she was brought up to the Solomons for Government work. Everyone who sailed in her became attached to her, as though to a living creature. During the war years one of the bravest and most enterprising men who went out in her was William

Billy Bennet, the handsome son of a Solomon Island mother and Billy Bennet, her English sailor husband. Young Billy was brave and intelligent and possessed the great gift of leadership, a mystique of his own which had an almost hypnotic effect on his men. He undertook some very daring exploits in the *Wai-ai* when, on several occasions, far behind enemy lines, the ship narrowly escaped disaster by lying in a concealed anchorage until cruising enemy ships went by. Billy was in command when the *Wai-ai* was surprised at anchor by a Japanese landing-craft which, as it came nearer, poured machine-gun fire into her. It was the end, and Billy carried out his orders. He drenched the deck and housing with petrol; Japanese bullets started the fire. Billy and his crew dived overboard and swam ashore to safety. The *Wai-ai* was blazing furiously when the Japanese approached her. She burned down to her water line and then sank at the anchorage.